Considering that he had sacked her
from her job, it might be thought that
when Cormac Daly offered Lynda
Groome another job instead, it meant
he was having twinges of conscience
about the situation. But, Lynda soon
discovered, it didn't mean any such
thing . . .

A WOMAN
IN LOVE

BY

LILIAN PEAKE

MILLS & BOON LIMITED
15–16 BROOK'S MEWS
LONDON W1A 1DR

First published 1984
Australian copyright 1984
Philippine copyright 1984
This edition 1984

© Lilian Peake 1984

ISBN 0 263 74656 9

Set in Monophoto Times 10 on 10 pt.
01–0684 – 59760

Made and printed in Great Britain by
Richard Clay (The Chaucer Press) Ltd,
Bungay, Suffolk

CHAPTER ONE

THE girl in the picture was beautiful. Her brown hair had been swept high, while the plunging neckline of her bright sleeveless dress showed a shape of which most women would be proud. Her mouth curved in an enticing smile and her arms were flung wide, inviting the reader to buy and buy again the products the company was promoting.

Lynda, contemplating her own photograph, was dismayed. The pocket-sized sales catalogue lay open on her desk. Her picture was spread boldly across the centre pages, and around her were displayed cookware and baking trays, dishes and pans.

Mandy, who occupied the desk alongside Lynda's, sighed her admiration. 'I can't see what's upsetting you. If I had a face like yours——'

'That's the point,' Lynda broke in. 'It's not my face, nor my personality. I haven't got that girl's poise, nor her sophistication. All that make-up they put on me . . .'

'Not to mention the fabulous jewellery,' Mandy added.

'That's no more real than she is,' Lynda retorted, pointing at the picture.

'But it's you!'

'It's no more me than you are, Mandy. Surely you know that?'

'Perhaps,' her friend returned with unexpected wisdom, 'there's a girl just like that inside you, screaming to get out.'

Lynda shook her head. Frowning, she confessed, 'I didn't want to pose for those pictures.'

'So why did you?' Mandy leaned on Lynda's desk, studying the girl in the advertisement.

'In the end,' Lynda answered, 'they persuaded me by offering money.'

Mandy looked up quickly. 'You didn't take it?'

'The cheque's right there in my bag. It came by post this morning.'

'That makes it worse. There's a company rule, didn't you know? No employee is allowed to appear in any of the promotions the company takes on. And accepting money for doing it—well, it's like signing your own notice to quit the job.'

'Why didn't the advertising people tell me?' Lynda asked, her fingers rigid against her cheek.

'Maybe they assumed you knew.'

'I've only been here eight weeks, so how could I if no one warned me? And I'm not blaming you,' she added hurriedly.

Mandy returned to her own desk. 'If I'd known what was going on, I'd have told you. A memo came round about six months ago—of course,' she remarked, frowning, 'you wouldn't know that, either. A girl from Sales called Amy posed in a sundress on a garden swing-seat they were promoting. She was out, without a job, in two days flat after the brochure appeared. That was when the rule was reissued.'

'Did she know the rule?'

Mandy nodded. 'But her boy-friend, Larry Chapman, persuaded her, saying they'd make sure she wasn't recognisable. Something about photographic trickery. But they let her down—said they thought she looked too good to hide her face.'

'It was Larry Chapman who persuaded me,' Lynda said, deeply distressed.

'You're not his girl-friend, are you?' Lynda shook her head. 'I only asked because it went round that that was his way of getting Amy off his back. He had another girl lined up.'

'He should have told me the rule,' Lynda exclaimed.

'Larry only really cares about his precious job, not about the company or his colleagues, and that includes you and me.' Mandy ran a fingernail lightly over the typewriter keys. 'I didn't think you were the kind to let money influence you, anyway.'

'It's just that I needed it.' Lynda sank into her chair. 'Not for myself—I can afford to live reasonably well on my salary. It's——' she paused '—family reasons,' she finished, deciding to keep to herself the reason why the offer of the money had overcome her reluctance to agree to Larry's request.

Mandy nodded. 'Why didn't they use a professional model?' she asked. 'That's what they usually do.'

'Larry told me I looked more like a typical user of the product they were promoting.'

Mandy laughed. 'You? Kitchenware? And in that dress? Don't look too closely at that picture, Lynda, but you're showing an awful lot of—you know.'

Lynda covered her face with her hand. 'I know. Isn't it terrible?'

There was a commotion at the main entrance door of the large office. The other employees, all at their desks, sat strangely still. A spiralling silence advanced, tornado-like, across the open-plan office. Searching for the cause of the charged atmosphere and heightened tension, Lynda saw in the doorway a man surrounded by other men. He was dark-haired and she guessed he was tall since he towered over his companions. In a group as he was, Lynda could see only his head and shoulders. But she was hardly conscious of the fact, since the impact of two steely-grey eyes robbed her of breath.

The owner of those eyes projected towards her such a stare that it knocked her poise into a pile of rubble. As he turned to go, he gave her a slicing side-glance and she wished she had had a mirror to discover just what there was about her to have earned such disparagement.

All around her, work was resumed, and Lynda turned to stare at Mandy. 'Who was that?' she whispered.

'The boss himself, Cormac Daly. Didn't you guess?'

'What was he doing here? Is that usual?'

Mandy lifted a shoulder. 'Now and then one of the senior people comes exploring the lower levels. But never Mr Daly—until now.'

'Have you ever met him?'

'Cormac Daly? Me? Insignificant Mandy Ash?' She smiled wryly, her small face glowing. 'What did you think of him?'

'I only really saw his eyes. If looks could kill, I'd be flat out down there on the floor.'

Mandy laughed. 'You're imagining things. He's got too much on his mind to pick out the newest girl on the staff and cut her down to size just for the hell of it. He's been away for a couple—no, three months altogether.'

'Abroad on business, I suppose?'

'Well, we heard he was off on vacation—a winter skiing holiday. The grapevine said he'd had an accident on the slopes.'

'So now he's back, which means he must have recovered from the accident?' Lynda commented.

'Looks like it. From this distance, he seemed all right, but I didn't like to stare.' Mandy grinned. 'And you only saw his eyes.'

Lynda sighed, shaking her head. 'I must have imagined he picked on me, as you said.'

'Unless it was your looks.'

'What looks? There's nothing special about me.'

'Isn't there?' Mandy pointed to the booklet. 'That shows you've got the lot.'

Lynda laughed. 'I told you, that isn't the real me. Anyway, he'd have had to be starved of women to have gone to all that trouble to track the girl in that photograph down.'

'If the rumour was right and he really did have an accident, he probably is—woman-starved, I mean.' Mandy frowned. 'There was a woman, someone said, who hurt him, but——'

'What woman?' asked Lynda, bewildered now. 'His wife? Has he been divorced, or something?'

'No, not divorced. He's not married, but someone said they saw him once with a beautiful female hanging on his arm. The grapevine said they'd split up, but no one knew why.'

The telephone extension on Lynda's desk shrilled

across the conversation. 'Lynda Groome here,' she told the caller.

'Miss Groome, this is Betty Peters, Mr Daly's secretary. Mr Daly would like to see you.'

Lynda's palm grew moist. 'When—when does he want me to come, Miss Peters?'

'Mrs Peters,' the voice corrected gently. 'In twenty minutes, please. We're two floors up. Come to my office first, will you? My name's on the door, fourth on the left.'

The receiver clattered to rest. 'I've got twenty minutes to live,' Lynda breathed.

'Mandy pointed to the phone. 'That was——?'

'Mr Daly's secretary. He wants to see me. Why, Mandy, why?'

'So maybe you weren't imagining things.' Mandy gave her a look of pity. 'Sooner you than me, Lynda. He's got the reputation of being as sympathetic as a wild animal mad with hunger, plus, when he's feeling kind, a bite as gentle as a crocodile's!'

'Now that really does cheer me up,' groaned Lynda, pressing her knuckles to her cheek. Mandy laughed but Lynda did not see the joke. She sank back on to her seat, flipping the booklet shut, only to reopen it immediately at the centre pages, thrusting them towards her friend.

'It's that photograph,' Lynda declared. 'I'm sure he's seen it. Mandy, I'm going to lose my job . . .'

Mandy shook her head: 'It doesn't take the chairman of the company to sack someone on our level. Someone from Personnel would do that.'

Lynda wished she could feel reassured. 'What happened with that other girl?' she asked.

'You mean who called her in? Mr White of Personnel. He deals with people like us.' She smiled broadly. 'I told you, it's your looks Mr Daly's fallen for. He'll probably eat out of your hand. He might be thinking of promoting you—you never know!'

With a smile at Lynda's 'you must be joking,' Mandy started to work.

Twenty minutes later, Lynda stood in Betty Peters'
office. The secretary was slim, brown-haired and in her
thirties. On her desk was a photograph of two smiling
children. Standing behind them was a well-built, equally
smiling man. Which could only mean, Lynda reasoned,
that the woman was happily married. And that must
surely also mean that she was not the 'beautiful female',
to whom Mandy had referred.

The secretary rose at once, saying, 'Mr Daly will see
you now,' and led her towards an adjoining door.

'Mrs Peters,' Lynda detained her momentarily, her
heart's low throb accelerating to a fast pound, 'isn't Mr
Daly the chairman?'

The secretary's smile held surprise. Her hand was on
the door-catch. 'But of course.'

'I only started here eight weeks ago, so ... Mrs
Peters,' Lynda lowered her voice, 'could you tell me
why he wants to see me?'

Shaking her head, the secretary opened the door and
encouraged her to enter.

'Why don't you ask me?' the man at the desk shot at
her over his shoulder. He had swivelled his seat
sideways and was half-reclining. He was completely at
ease and in total command. The rest of him was
obviously outstretched, although Lynda could not see
for certain. There were his eyes again, running through
her. The steeliness which had sliced into her half an
hour ago had not left them. It seemed, if anything, to
have intensified.

'Sit down, Miss Groome.' It was a directive, not an
invitation. Since he had motioned to the upright chair
opposite him, she took it, holding on to her handbag as
if it were a life-support machine.

Watching her, he stretched out a hand to pick up a
folder from the desk top. It's my personal file, she
thought, he's been checking up on me as if I were a
criminal! Her anger seemed to give him a certain
satisfaction as she caught a glinting glance a moment
before he concentrated on the papers the file contained.

Head down but with her eyes secretly lifted, she

studied the man. His brown hair swept low across his brow, having a ruffled look as if he often raked it back in irritation. His brows were pulled inward to a frown of concentration, this in itself giving emphasis to the positive statement of his nose.

Lines curved from nostrils to the commencement of his jaw, bracketing a resolute mouth. The strong line of his cheekbones told of an obstinate and tenacious nature, but it was his eyes, which were now swinging unexpectedly to hers, which told Lynda in unequivocal terms that he was not a man to be pushed around.

An uplifted eyebrow caused her colour to rise at being caught in the act of watching him. He proceeded to repay the compliment boldly and without scruple, making no attempt to hide his scrutiny as she had done hers.

Whether he liked the cheek structure which gave an oval shape to her face, the long-lashed eyes, the faintly tip-tilted nose, she could not tell. His expressionless face told no tales. But when it came to her mouth, his eyes conveyed a masculine message as they lingered on its fullness. Her lips, parted slightly on a soundless gasp, told him silently of her annoyance at his audacity.

He was not slow in lowering his gaze to conduct a long-distance examination of the rest of her. He was a good few feet away, but she felt her skin prickle as though, by remote control, he had actually made physical contact.

'Stand up, Miss Groome.'

The order was given so curtly she obeyed, but she infused every rising movement with a reluctance which told him clearly of her deep resentment. With another raking look, he reached out to open a drawer, taking from it the dreaded booklet.

So she had been right after all—that photograph was the reason for her summons to the presence of the man at the top! It could only mean one thing—she was on her way out. Well, she would fight every retreating inch of the way!

The pages were open at the centre spread. His eyes

withdrew from contemplating it to flick insultingly over
her. 'Who got you to pose in this fashion?'

It was a knife-thrust which she would parry. 'The
studio manager. But that girl isn't me, Mr Daly. It's an
artificial person from top to bottom. As you've just
said, it's a pose, it's false.'

'I disagree. It shows a side of you which it probably
gives you a virtuous feeling to disown, but which no
amount of denying on your part will exorcise.' His lids
flickered low as he said, 'Why bother? It arouses a
man's curiosity, challenges him, makes him want to seek
out and find that,' he tapped the photograph, 'in *that*,'
he gestured towards her. 'Now, sit down, Miss
Groome.' He had, at the flick of a mental switch,
turned from concupiscent male to clinically-detached
businessman.

If he had meant to disconcert and humiliate, Lynda
thought furiously, then he had succeeded. 'That still
isn't the real me,' she declared as a final protest. Her
statement went unheeded.

'Tell me,' he glanced up from the file, 'why did you
leave your job with the cinema chain?'

'I wasn't happy there. And I felt they weren't paying
me enough.'

He nodded, reading another letter. 'Why did you quit
this next job with your local theatrical company?'

'Well,' she rubbed her forehead with her fingers, 'I
enjoyed the work, but they were struggling financially.'

'In other words, you were again after more money?'
She nodded. 'So you moved here. Are you satisfied with
your salary?'

Her eyes found his with some surprise. 'I am. Why?'

'Yet you felt the need for more and found it by
posing for this Kitchenware launch?'

The hard-hitting inquisition was sandpapering her
nerves. He was getting to the point of it with such
agonising slowness, she wanted to scream. And how did
he know about the financial angle? Maybe, she
reasoned, as levelly as her mixed-up reasoning powers
would allow, it was a trick question.

He looked her over and seemed to see with satisfaction the dismay in her eyes, the over-heated cheeks. 'You realise by doing this that you've placed your job with us in serious jeopardy?'

'I didn't know the company rule then,' she exclaimed, her voice rising. 'No one told me until this morning when the booklet was distributed. And even then it was my friend Mandy, not Larry Chapman. The memo about the rule came out before I started here. How could I know?'

'The memo is displayed on the notice-board in the staff restaurant. Personnel also hands out the company rules to a newcomer on his or her first day.'

'I didn't even know there was a notice-board, so how could I have seen it? And I haven't got round yet to reading the rules. I've only been here eight weeks.'

'I'm aware of that,' he returned coldly. 'Larry Chapman—are you his latest girl-friend?'

'You mean a liability he wants to get rid of like the last time this happened? To a girl called Amy, I was told. No.'

A sound penetrated of a door clicking shut. In Lynda's head it was like the sound of thunder as Cormac Daly said, 'As from the end of the day, your employment with this company will be over. You will be given your salary, which will include an amount in place of a month's notice.'

Lynda asked, aghast, 'But why, Mr Daly? I've done well in my eight weeks here, haven't I? Ask all the people I've worked for in the company.'

'I have. They agree with your statement.'

'So why sack a good employee?'

'You broke the company rule, Miss Groome,' he answered inflexibly.

'I told you, it was in ignorance. Didn't you hear me?' She started up, stretched over, and seized the opened booklet. Her furious fingers ripped it to pieces. She dropped them into a nearby waste bin. 'Now it's gone.' Her hands were shaking as she retrieved her bag which

had fallen to the floor. Rising, she stood waiting, face
flushed, eyes pleading, hoping.

'Unfortunately for you,' his eyes flashed as he
reached into a drawer and extracted another copy,
holding it up, 'there are thousands of others, many of
them already distributed.'

His stare hardened, a muscle worked in his jaw.
What, she wondered, should she do now? Hold up her
head and leave? Since he stayed silent, she turned
around, straightening her shoulders and swinging her
legs in a striding defiance.

Once outside, she knew her self-defensive dignity
would collapse, and at the door, she glanced back. He
was looking, not at her, but at the girl in the picture.

In record time, Lynda made it down to the basement
and Larry Chapman's office. It was a glassed-in section
of a large, high display area. There were backdrops,
lights slung everywhere, small sets like parts of a home,
theatrical yet deceptively real.

Larry was sorting through photographs at his desk.
His over-long sandy hair looked as though he had not
combed it for days. His pale-skinned face turned
towards her as she burst in. He was not good-looking,
but there was something about him, Lynda perceived,
that some girls would go for, although she was not one
of them.

On the desk was a pile of the booklets. She seized one
and opened it at the centre pages. 'You know what
you've done?' she threw at him. 'You've got me fired
from my job! This,' she stabbed at the picture of herself,
'this was against the rules. You knew it but you didn't
tell me—I could hit you for that!'

He rested on the desk top on his palms, shoulders
lifted high on a kind of continuing shrug. 'So I knew
the rule. So I thought you knew it, too.'

'Do you really think I'd have let you persuade me if I
had known? You think I'd have risked losing my job
just for that?'

'Who knows what a girl will do for a bit of extra

money? You accepted the fee I offered, didn't you? How can you blame me if I thought you'd be willing to take the risk for the extra cash? Anyway, the boss is away——'

'He's back. Today. He's just sacked me!' Her voice had risen and Larry Chapman pretended to cover his ears.

He straightened. 'You mean *the* boss, Cormac Daly? What was he doing talking to someone as low down the scale as little Lynda Groome?'

'You can stop sneering, Larry. And withdraw the "little". I'm twenty-three and——'

'And certainly not so little.' His eyes were insolently all over her.

Lynda wanted to curl into herself, then remembered how much of her shape he had persuaded her to reveal during that photographic session.

The telephone rang and Larry reached out for it. 'Studio here. Yes, speaking.' He listened and his eyes swung to Lynda. 'A fee? Yeah, I paid Miss Groome a fee, Mr Daly. How much?' He stated the amount. 'She's down here, now—aren't you, sweetheart? Speak to her? Okay, I'll hand over.' His pale eyes gleamed as Lynda flinched from the touch of his fingers as she took over.

'Why did you have to tell him I'm here,' she offered, annoyed by the waver in her voice.

'What a surprise to find you there, Miss Groome,' the cutting voice of Cormac Daly scraped her ear. 'So you're not Chapman's latest girl-friend. Do you really expect me to believe that now?'

'What I said was true, Mr Daly. There's nothing between Larry and me. Except that I'm——' furious with him, she had been about to say.

'Spare me the details. Why, Miss Groome, didn't you come clean with me when I asked if you'd been paid for posing?'

'You never actually asked me,' she answered, indignant now.

'Don't mince words. I gave you every chance of admitting you'd received payment. It was quite a sum, wasn't it?' The voice was silky now. 'Almost as much as they would have given an experienced model. How hard did you bargain with him, Miss Groome?'

'I did *not* bargain! He used the money to persuade me.'

'Money which you needed, of course.' The silkiness flicked sparks.

'Who doesn't, these days?' she countered.

'But you had a special reason.'

It was not a question, so she gave no reply.

The caller rang off. Lynda clattered the receiver down and turned on Larry. 'I could wring your neck for getting me fired!' she cried, and ran from his office.

As Lynda arrived at her desk, Mandy looked up from her work. 'Good news or bad?' she asked.

Lynda shook her head, compressing her lips. Mandy nodded understandingly and concentrated on her typing. After ten minutes of flicking aimlessly through the letters on her desk which were still waiting to be answered, she said to her friend under cover of the noise around them:

'That rumour that he'd had an accident was wrong. He seemed all right to me.'

Again, Mandy nodded. After a few minutes, Lynda told her, 'Today's my last day.'

Mandy's hands slid from the typewriter to her lap. 'He hasn't sacked you? He couldn't, Lyn, not just like that!' She watched the slow, sad nod. 'Didn't you tell him you didn't know that rule?'

'He told me all the different ways I should have heard about it.'

'You're a good worker, Lyn. Doesn't he know that?'

'He knows. He checked up on me. The feed-back was good, but it made no difference.' Her fist clenched on a folder and her head swung to her colleague. 'That man is the most unfeeling, callous, insensitive brute——' The ringing of her extension cut into her outburst.

'Yes?' Lynda answered dully.

'Got a date for tonight?' Larry Chapman asked.

'I don't know how you've got the nerve to ask that after losing me my job.'

'You told the boss there was nothing between us, honey. That was a challenge. You do something to me. Give me the chance and I'll make you feel the same way about me.'

'Stop talking in tired clichés, Larry, and just get out of my life,' she snapped. 'You're going to, anyway, after today, because I'm leaving, thanks to you.'

'That's okay,' he answered cheerfully.

'You got some other girl the sack by your dirty tricks, Larry. But you had a reason for that bit of nastiness, didn't you? What have I ever done to you?'

'Nothing, so far, honey, but meet me tonight and we'll soon put that right.'

Lynda slammed down the phone.

'I hate Larry Chapman,' Mandy sympathised. 'I should have warned you about him.'

Lynda shook her head. 'He's lost me my job, yet he's just asked me for a date! I went straight down there to tell him what I thought of him, and while I was there, Mr Daly rang down.' She recounted what had happened.

'It doesn't matter now,' said Mandy realistically. 'You're on your way out, aren't you?'

'I certainly am,' Lynda agreed, dejection tugging at her spirits. For a long time, she tried persuading herself that it really didn't matter, as her friend had said, but it was a useless exercise.

It mattered, it mattered a lot, she told herself, and it was not only the loss of her job. It went deeper than that—so deep, in fact, she could not dredge far enough down into her feelings to guess the reason.

The rest of the morning she spent wondering despondently how long it would take her to find other work. At lunchtime, Mandy's efforts to cheer her up brought no results.

As the afternoon progressed, Lynda told her friend, 'It's eating into me that Mr Daly's sacked me just for that.' She indicated the drawer into which the booklet had been pushed. 'Before I go, I'll *have* to do something to tell the man just what I think of him.'

Mandy smiled and shook her head. 'No chance. He'll have gone, won't he? I know, write him a memo for delivery tomorrow when you're not here.'

'Not here?' Lynda looked around her. Only then did it really strike home that in an hour's time her means of earning a living would have been snatched away. One hour? she thought. Is that all that's left? Turning to Mandy, she said, 'I don't know why I'm sitting here working. Sixty more minutes——'

'And you'll be a free woman,' Mandy joked. She looked up at the wall clock. 'Why don't you pack up now?'

'I think I'm going to take your advice.' Lynda collected her work into a pile and asked her friend to hand it in in the morning to the person who had given her the letters to answer.

'Ring me some time, won't you,' said Mandy, a little tearfully.

Lynda nodded, gathering her belongings. 'It's been nice knowing you—and I do mean that. I'll keep in touch.' She looked around and saw all the others busy with their work, secure in their jobs. Anger swirled inside her and she made for the door.

With the minimum of fuss, Personnel handed over everything that was due to her. They seemed to have been notified in advance and had it all prepared, which stirred the cauldron of her anger even more. Cormac Daly had plainly made sure that her employment with the company was well and truly terminated.

Looking at the envelopes and documents in her hands, she thought, All right, since I'm no longer an employee, I can really tell him what I think of him!

Indignation raced with her up the stairs. Breathless, she arrived at Betty Peters' door. Entering, she found the room was empty. The communicating door stood open and the sound of voices came through.

I don't care who's with him, Lynda thought, raking

in her handbag for the firm's cheque which Larry Chapman had sent her, he's going to get this thrown right back at him! Bursting into the chairman's office, she ran the few steps to his desk and flung the cheque down.

'Now you've got it back!' she cried. 'Keep it—it's the company's money. Now maybe you'll understand that I posed for that picture for the love of the——' Company, she had been going to say, but it stayed in her throat.

Cormac Daly was standing beside his desk, his secretary's hand on his shoulder, steadying him. His weight had been taken by the crutches fitted around his elbows. His left leg was held stiffly at a slight angle and appeared to be encased in plaster. Which meant, Lynda thought dazedly, that the rumour about an accident was true.

He was staring at her, harshness in his gaze. 'What the hell do you think you're doing, Miss Groome? I don't recall inviting you in.'

'I'm sorry. I had no idea you were . . .'

'Incapacitated is a suitably neutral word,' he suggested gratingly. 'Mrs Peters, return that cheque to Miss Groome.'

'If you give it back to me,' Lynda declared, 'I'll tear it up!'

'I don't think you will. I'm quite sure your need for money will surmount such a dramatic display of wounded pride.'

Mrs Peters approached with a kindly smile, offering her the cheque.

'If you tear that up,' the incisive voice of her ex-employer came at her, 'I shall personally write you another. Destroy that, and I'll destroy you.'

'I don't work for you any more, Mr Daly. I refuse to——'

'Take it, Miss Groome,' his tone was deceptively soft. 'You'll need the money, won't you?'

He was right. She would be foolish to reject it, but she wanted to gnash her teeth with mortification. He

had won the brief battle. Folding the cheque, she
pushed it back into her bag.

'Do you have a job in mind?' Cormac Daly asked as
she reached the door.

Her head went up with a return of the pride he had
humbled. 'I don't, but there's no need for you to worry
about that.'

'Someone I know badly needs secretarial help.' He
turned, not without pain, to open a drawer, pointing
towards its interior. 'Copy out that address, Betty, and
give it to Miss Groome.'

Betty Peters scanned the address, and glanced at her
employer, who nodded. Then she did as he had ordered.
With a smile, she handed over the slip of paper.

Lynda scanned it and protested, 'But this is some
way outside London. I couldn't travel there every day
from where I live.'

'I should try it, Miss Groome, if I were you,' Betty
Peters urged, turning to assist her employer as he made
to move across the room.

The silence made her look up. Cormac Daly's broad
shoulders were braced against the pressure of the
crutches. His head was high and his eyes held a
challenge.

Which, Lynda thought with a spurt of comprehension
that surprised herself, was surely how he faced every
difficulty in life, including an accident which had left
him disabled and evidently in pain.

'Thank you,' she told him with cold politeness, 'but I
doubt if I'll bother,' and pushing the paper into her
pocket, she left them.

The long week merged into the weekend. In her
telephone conversations with her mother, Lynda had
held back from telling her about the loss of her job. It
would have worried her, and worry was the last thing
she wished to inflict.

On Saturday morning, she rang her mother, having
decided to visit her at her South London flat. As the
Underground train stopped and started, whining its

way through the seemingly endless tunnel, Lynda took
out the slip of paper which Mrs Peters had given her. It
had been much handled in those empty days since she
had become unemployed.

The address was of a place in the countryside some
thirty miles north-west of London. No name was given,
nor any telephone number. The only way in which she
could make contact was to go there, present herself on
the doorstep and say—what could she say?

'I've been told there's a vacancy for a secretary here.
Please will you give me the job?'

The situation was so improbable that Lynda pushed
the address away yet again. When she had recovered
from the tumble her self-confidence had taken as a
result of her ex-employer's precipitate and harsh action,
she would go to an employment agency.

They would, she realised, need references. Surely the
man would not be so vindictive as to give her a bad
one? Hadn't he inflicted enough damage by depriving
her of a job she liked and which was well paid?

Her mother received her with pleasure and affection.
Her hair was greying, but her round face and bright
eyes made her look the picture of middle-aged health. It
had taken her a long time to reconcile herself to being a
widow after her beloved husband had died. Lynda, too,
had mourned the loss of her father for a long time.

Taking the empty space beside her mother on the
couch, she watched the once able hands move the
knitting yarn round the needles.

'I'm fine, love,' her mother declared in answer to the
customary query. It was the reply she invariably gave.
The fact that her hands were becoming increasingly
affected by arthritis, thus threatening her sole means of
livelihood, was never mentioned to anyone except her
daughter, and even then it would be brushed aside as of
little consequence.

The income Rose Groome derived from the sale of
knitted garments to friends and varied customers was
lessening, not through incompetence, but a slowly
diminishing ability to carry out their orders. In fact, the

demand for the handmade garments was increasing, and it was this growing demand that worried Lynda so much.

After the familiar mother–daughter exchanges, Lynda reached out and took the work from her mother, taking over the knitting pattern at the same time. Rose smiled gratefully and rested back, momentarily closing her eyes. Her hands lay curled stiffly in her lap and her arms lay loosely as if they, too, were needing a rest.

'I'll get us some coffee in a moment, dear,' Mrs Groome said, once more her bright self. 'That jacket you're working on is for a friend of a friend of Matty's.'

Lynda laughed. 'Your fame is spreading,' she answered, secretly wondering how her mother could manage to hold such a heavy garment.

'How's work?' Rose called from the kitchen.

Lynda's hands slowed to a stop. She hated having to lie to her mother, but it was, she told herself, in the interests of her mother's health. If she told her mother the truth, it would make her say, You mustn't give me any more money until you've found one again. And cutting out the weekly allowance she made to her mother would happen over her own dead body.

Over the clatter of cups, Lynda answered, 'It's—it's shaping up nicely.'

Her mother appeared in the doorway. 'Are you talking about that jacket or your job?' she queried, smiling.

Lynda frowned concentratedly at the stitches her fingers were creating. 'My job, of course.' She had actually managed an answering smile.

Rose disappeared again. At the end of the row, Lynda lowered the knitting to her lap. Looking around the high-ceilinged room, its old but comfortable chairs rescued, like much of the flat's other furniture, from the house in which she had lived with her parents for so many years, Lynda wondered how she was going to manage to give her mother the financial help she needed, and at the same time provide for her own needs, too. The three rooms she rented cost less to run than this ground floor apartment of her mother's, but add the two together, and what would be left to feed and clothe herself?

Her mother had her own allowances, of course, and she herself would receive some kind of financial benefit, but there would be nothing like the same amount left over as she had managed to give her mother while she still had a job to go to.

Again, she searched in her bag for the puzzling, anonymous address. Should she go to this mysterious place and stand begging on the doorstep for a job which, for all she knew, might not even exist? Or if it had existed, might have been filled?

It would be a risk, she reasoned, because if someone else had been appointed, her train fare would have been wasted—and that, she thought, pushing the address back into place, would be a calamitous waste of money.

'What's that, dear?' asked Rose, carrying in the tray and handing it over with some relief to her daughter. 'A letter? You were putting it away so quickly, it makes me wonder if it was a love letter!' She smiled, resuming her seat. 'Have you heard from John?' Her bright eyes rested hopefully on her daughter.

'Not for weeks. There's nothing between us now. You know that.'

Rose nodded, stirring her coffee and drinking while her daughter stared into the depths of her own.

'I wish you had a boy-friend, all the same,' Rose commented wistfully. 'I wish you could get married. Then,' brightly, 'I could have some grandchildren. Before,' she put aside her cup and examined her hands, 'these get too stiff and silly to hold them.'

There was a rush of tears behind Lynda's eyes. 'Oh, Mum,' she shook her head, 'don't dream like that. One day, maybe, I'll meet someone. But these days, women decide to put off having a family for years. They have careers. . . .'

'You won't do that,' her mother responded confidently. 'You love children too much to do such a foolish thing.'

Lynda smiled and shook her head. 'It's no good. There's not a man in sight I want to go out with, let alone marry.'

'Is that the truth, dear?' Rose's saddened eyes sought her daughter's.

After the merest, inexplicable hesitation, Lynda heard herself say, 'Yes, Mother, it's the truth.'

CHAPTER TWO

A WEEK passed of fretting and getting nowhere. Two of
the six agencies Lynda called on offered a faint hope of
holiday jobs. Not one of them had materialised.

Lynda had cleaned her flat, washed clothes and
furnishings and typed applications for jobs she had seen
advertised in newspapers. She had gone window-
shopping, wandered round the large London stores,
admired everything that was financially as out of her
reach as distant galaxies.

Arriving back, she drew out an atlas to look up on a
map the place mentioned in the address she had been
given. It took her a few minutes to track down the exact
area. Then she found the place name, in type that was
large enough to indicate that it was the size of a town,
probably a small one.

With a sigh, she closed the book and replaced it on
the shelf. Knowing where it was did nothing to resolve
the problem that had been tormenting her from the
moment the piece of paper had been put into her hand.
Should she, or should she not, go there?

One evening she took out the copy of the booklet in
which her picture had appeared. She had brought it
home with her—compliments of the company, Larry
Chapman had said. Staring at herself, she saw for the
first time that it was after all an attractive shot.

The phone rang, bringing to her body a nervous
shudder of guilt. Why, she thought, going to the
phone, should I feel guilty? I've reaped the rewards of
that particular incident. I've paid for it and it's
behind me.

'Lynda?'

It was as much as she could do to stop herself from
putting down the receiver. 'What do you want, Larry?'

'Got a job yet?'

Unwilling to tell him the truth, she answered, 'I'm—er—awaiting decisions.'

'Which means you haven't. I've been let down by a model. Nothing difficult—just looking beautiful on a sunbed. Want the job?'

'I don't. . . .' She checked her words. Where would it get her if she refused? If she accepted, at least she would be able to continue to help her mother without tearing her mind apart wondering what else she could sacrifice to keep up her weekly contribution.

'Okay, you don't. You don't want the money, either, that's it, then.' Larry did not ring off. It was almost as though he was waiting for her protest.

Lynda wished she was in a position to slam him off the line, but her need was too great for that. 'It's nothing indecent, is it?' she asked.

'Indecent? Now, would I ask a nice girl like you if it was?'

Overcoming her habitual reluctance to haggle, she queried, 'How much, Larry?'

'The fee? Same as before.'

How hard did you bargain with him, Miss Groome? Cormac Daly's words wound themselves round her mind. Well, this time she'd do just that! Cormac Daly was no longer her employer. She would never see him again, so even though, in a sense, she would be working for his company, he wouldn't be able to throw that insinuation at her again.

Swallowing hard, she pressed, 'I'd need more than that, Larry. After all, you lost me my job.'

'So you're not above doing a deal now, honey? Has being destitute brought you that low?'

'I'm not destitute or low. It's just that I've come to know my own worth.' She added with sugar-sweetness, 'A model's let you down, isn't that right? I could come and get you out of trouble at a moment's notice. Right?'

There was an admiring laugh from the other end. 'Being out of a job's certainly hardened you up, honey! So I'll give you what I'd have given the model. Plus the cost of getting there.'

'It's a deal. When do you want me?'

'Always and for ever,' he joked. 'Come tomorrow afternoon as early as you can make it.'

It seemed as if no time had passed since the last time she had entered the tower block which contained the offices of Daly Enterprises. It seemed right that Mick, the doorkeeper, should lift his hand and smile. But it hit a discordant note when he asked, with a guarded look, 'Couldn't keep away from the place, eh, miss? Come to see Mr Daly?'

It was correct—good security, she supposed—that he should question her, but it made her realise with a shock that he had been advised of her leaving the company's employment.

Lynda frowned, affecting a laugh. 'What would someone like me be doing, Mick, going to see a man like Mr Daly? I'm not so lucky. I've come to see Mr Chapman. Standing in for a model who couldn't make it.'

Mick nodded, apparently satisfied. As she made for the stairs to the lower floor, she glanced back to see him speaking quietly into a telephone. He was checking up that what she had said was true!

Reason, with difficulty, overcame the rush of indignation. That was his job, wasn't it? Although she couldn't help wondering if he had been especially detailed by the man at the top to make a special check on a young woman named Lynda Groome. . . .

'Good,' said Larry, the moment she appeared in the doorway, 'I'll give you cash in advance. That should keep you sweet.'

He pulled a cheque-book from his desk drawer and wrote in the amount they had agreed between them. She looked over his shoulder. 'It's your personal cheque, Larry. Last time, it was the company's. Why the difference?'

'I'll get it out of them, don't worry.'

Taking the cheque, she frowned. 'What did you mean by saying it should keep me sweet? You told me there was nothing indecent about it.'

'You wouldn't call wearing a two-piece and lying on a sunbed indecent, would you, honey?' Lynda started shaking her head. 'Ah, come on, it's getting on for the year two thousand. Who gave you your Victorian attitudes?'

'You should have warned me, Larry! I'm angry——'

'You look it, with that fat cheque clutched in your hot little hand.' He turned away, sorting through a pile of clothes, pulling out two multi-coloured pieces of material. 'These your size?' He measured her visually. 'Should fit. Might be a bit small, but that's a plus. You're a better shape than most models we get here.'

'You don't expect me to wear those?' she demanded.

He uttered a deep sigh, removed the cheque from her fingers and made 'go away' signs with his hand.

'I need that money!' she cried, retrieving the cheque. 'I'll do it, as long as you promise to——'

'I've paid you an experienced model's rate for the job. A professional wouldn't have made any conditions, just got on with the work.'

Lynda stared again at the amount. There was no arguing with the fact she badly needed the financial boost it would give to her almost non-existent bank account.

With a sigh, she pocketed the piece of paper. 'Where's the changing room? I've forgotten.'

Some time later, Lynda lay on the inflated sunbed, neck supported by her elbow and hand. Her hair hung silkily and blew in the gentle, simulated breeze. The rest of her reclined in the lazy-seeming fashion which Larry required. Although she appeared to be relaxed, she was far from being so. Repeatedly loosening reluctant muscles was, she had discovered, a painful business.

'Put your hand here—no there.' Larry bent down and placed her long fingers against an expanse of curving feminine thigh. 'Come on, honey, not much longer . . .' He turned sharply and stared over his shoulder.

There was an anxious, 'Hey Larry!' from across the studio—a warning from the make-up girl. The figure of a man filled the doorway, a man supported by crutches, face pale with fury. Steel-grey eyes moved from the horrified gaze of the reclining girl to the lingering hand of the studio manager crouching beside her.

There was a silence so crackling it was like a fire just lit.

Cormac Daly snapped, 'Get up, Miss Groome—*if* you can tear yourself away from Mr Chapman!'

Lynda scrambled to her feet. 'I've been working,' she declared. 'A model couldn't come, so Larry asked me to help him out.'

'I'm sure he did.' The sarcasm flashed in his eyes. 'How much are you paying this girl, Chapman?'

'As much as I'd have paid a model.'

'Halve it.'

'Why?' Lynda cried. 'I've done a good job.'

Steel glinted in Cormac Daly's eyes as he carried out a swift appraisal of her figure. 'I'm sure you have. With all the assets you possess, how could you not?'

Hating his look, Lynda seized a gown and swung it round her. 'He's already paid me, so he can't halve the amount. And,' her tone indicated it was the end of the matter, 'he paid me out of his own account.'

Larry added hurriedly, 'I intend claiming it back from the company, sir. I often do it that way.'

'This is one occasion, Mr Chapman, when the company will not reimburse you.' Cormac Daly's glance slewed narrowly to Lynda.

Larry's hand came out. 'Sorry, honey. Give me back my cheque. I'll buy you a present some time.'

'I need the money, Larry,' Lynda protested, near to tears. 'That's the only reason I agreed to do this work. And,' she added, 'you agreed to pay my fare here.'

'Your tune doesn't change, does it, Miss Groome? For ever in pursuit of money. There's no need to bother Mr Chapman for the cost of your journey.' Cormac Daly reached with difficulty into his inner pocket and withdrew a brown leather wallet. He did not ask her how much she needed, just took out a handful of high-value notes and held them out. 'Take these. And,' he taunted, 'this money comes from *my* personal account.'

Drawing the robe more closely around her, she said, 'Keep—' No, in the circumstances 'keep them' was one thing she could not throw at him. Clenching her teeth, she crossed the studio, wondering why his gaze had dropped as she approached. Glancing down, she saw that, at every other step she took, her left leg appeared through the unfastened opening of the robe.

Colouring with anger and humiliation, she accepted the money, hate for the man showing in her deeply blue eyes.

'Aren't you going to count them?' he mocked, as she turned away.

Turning back, she flashed, 'When you're as hard up as I am, you're not in a position to reject money that's due to you, however much you long to!'

'Get yourself an honest job of work to do, Miss Groome,' he tossed at her back. 'I gave you an address. Contact the man.'

'How do you know I haven't?' she retorted, swinging round.

'If you had, I'm certain you wouldn't be here. Your references are impeccable.'

'Then why did you sack me?'

His cold look and omission to answer made her shoulders droop as she entered the changing room.

'Destroy all film which you've taken of Miss Groome,' she heard Cormac Daly instruct.

'All of it? Mr Daly, it'll be a terrible waste! As a model, she's superb. With her decorating that sunbed, it'll sell a million!'

'Destroy it, Mr Chapman,' was the final order given by the chairman of the company just before he took himself painfully on his way.

Arriving home, Lynda padded barefoot about her flat, having swung her feet free of sandals. She found it impossible to stay in one place for more than a few moments. Indignation compressed her lips, resentment smouldered in her chest.

The man was a despot, a tyrant, ... He was

obviously under the impression that he could still control the direction in which her life was going, in spite of the fact that he did not employ her any more. Well, he was wrong—she would prove to him, and most important to herself, that he was wrong. She would get that man out of her hair if it killed her!

Eating a light lunch, Lynda made the journey to her mother's place. It was time, she had decided, that her mother heard the truth about her situation. It was a weekday, and this alone would tell her mother that something was wrong. She had not telephoned in advance because explanations, she reasoned, were better made face to face.

Using the key her mother had given her, she entered the hall, calling out as she closed the door, 'It's okay, Mum. And before you get worried, I'm fine.' She put her head round the door of her mother's living-room, her smile fading as she saw her mother's appearance.

In the past year, since they had lived apart, Lynda had always phoned her mother to make sure that it was convenient for her to call. She respected her mother's privacy and her mother meticulously repaid the compliment.

'Lynda?' Rose Groome started up from her resting position against the back of the couch. Her stiff fingers reached anxiously for the discarded knitting. 'What a fright you gave me, coming at this time!'

It was not the fright, Lynda perceived, that had given her mother's face the wan look, the air of lethargy as if she were fighting an impossible battle. She was shocked by her mother's appearance of self-neglect. Always, in the past and until now, her mother had cared for her looks, dressing neatly, using make-up to enhance her still attractive features.

So she had caught her mother unawares, off guard and revealing just how much of a toll her increasing incapacity was taking.

'What's wrong?' Lynda hurried to her mother's side. Rose smiled, the dejection clearing away from her eyes. 'Wrong, dear? Nothing, nothing at all. I'm fine, can't you see?'

'No, I can't see, Mother.' It was a mother–to–daughter reprimand, making Rose smile. 'What I can see is that every time I've come to see you, I've warned you I was coming and you've put on an excellent performance.' She took over her mother's knitting. 'I was worried about you before—I'm really anxious about you now.'

Rose smoothed her unattended grey-flecked hair. 'Don't you think I should be worried about you, dear? You look pale and tired. And what are you doing here at this time of day?'

Lynda put aside the knitting. 'That's what I came to tell you. Shall we talk over a cup of tea?' She went to the kitchen, her mother following.

While Lynda put on the kettle, Rose arranged cups and saucers on a circular, flowered tray. Lynda was amused by the action. 'Now I'm here, you're making an effort to put out pretty things!' She turned her mother's short, slim figure to the door. 'Now go and pretty yourself up.'

'Put on my act, dear?' Rose's smile was bright in her pale face.

'I didn't mean that,' Lynda laughed, kissing her mother's cheek. 'But a bit of make-up, your pink jacket—it'll do wonders for my morale, let alone yours.'

Having taken her daughter's advice, Rose Groome joined her in the living-room. 'Do you approve of your old mother now?' she asked, smiling.

'You called yourself old, Mother, I didn't. And of course I approve of you. There's never been a time when I haven't.'

Lynda placed a cup of tea carefully in her mother's awkward grasp. It pained her to see the hands that once had been so long and slender curled stiffly in such a way. Her mother, who had loved so steadfastly and cared so well for her husband and child, deserved a better fortune than this.

'Well, Lynda dear, we're drinking our tea. You

promised to talk over it, and I'm waiting.' Mrs Groome produced her brisk, 'mothering' voice. In the past, it had never failed to bring a rebellious daughter to her senses, no matter what kind of phase she had been passing through.

Lynda smiled to herself, for it had the same effect inside her now, but never for the world would she let her mother know. She sobered quickly, remembering the news she had to tell.

Putting her cup on the tray, she began, 'I'm out of a job.'

'I knew there was something wrong!' Rose handed Lynda her empty cup. 'Since when, dear?'

'Two or three weeks. It wasn't my fault—I broke a company rule. I hadn't been there long, so how was I expected to know it?'

'Which rule was this, Lynda?' Rose had taken up her knitting and was apparently working out a difficult stitch.

'The studio manager asked if I'd pose for a promotion picture. He said I looked the "domestically-minded little woman" type.'

'He was wrong, quite wrong,' Rose Groome muttered to the row of stitches with which she had started to wrestle. 'Did you do what he wanted?'

'Yes, I did.' Lynda threw a quick, sideways glance at her mother. 'What was wrong with that?'

'There must have been something, if you lost your job because of it.'

'I told you, there was a rule. Do you want to see the picture?'

The knitting hit Rose's lap. 'You know I do. When have I ever not wanted to see a picture of you?'

Lynda rummaged in the shopping bag she had brought with her. 'It's in this booklet.' She opened it out. 'Here, on the centre page.' Her mother eagerly took it.

'It's lovely, Lynda, it's really good of you.'

'You—you don't think I'm showing just a bit too much of——?'

'Of your curves, dear?' Rose laughed. 'Maybe you are, just a bit. But if it's meant to sell something, with a beautiful girl like you inviting people to buy, those baking tins and trays should sell very well indeed.'

Lynda was relieved to hear her mother's reassuring words. 'All the same, I'm now out of work because of that. You can keep it, Mum,' she added listlessly.

'Who sacked you, Lynda?'

'Would you believe it if I told you—the chairman himself?'

Rose laughed disbelievingly. 'No, I wouldn't.'

'He did, Mother, just like that. He was furious! You see, I accepted the fee which Larry Chapman gave me. After all, he said he would have had to pay a model. I— I tried to give the cheque back to Mr Daly.'

'Who's Mr Daly, dear?' The needles were clicking again.

'The chairman,' answered Lynda with a touch of impatience that her mother had not guessed.

'What was he doing, talking to a new arrival on the staff like you? Why didn't someone lower down——'

Lynda shook her head. 'That what Mandy and I couldn't understand. Mandy's been there for over three years and she said she's never known it happen before.'

There was a short silence and Lynda rested back her head.

'You should have told me about this earlier,' her mother said quietly. 'I know what you're going to say. You didn't want to worry me.' She smiled. 'You can't fool your mother. I knew there was something wrong, but I just waited for you to tell me.'

Lynda apologised. 'I've been trying to find work. So far, nobody's been inviting.'

'Because you were sacked from your last job?'

'How did you guess?' Lynda responded tiredly. After a pause, she said, 'I've got an address. No name, no phone number, just the address.' She studied her mother's profile, but Mrs Groome just went on knitting. 'Mr Daly gave it to me.' Her mother still did not respond. 'He said there was someone at the place who needed a secretary.'

'In that case, Mr Daly can't be all bad, can he?' This time it was Lynda who stayed silent. 'Have you made contact with the person?'

'Not yet.' She sat up. 'It's commuter country, by train or car. Now what do you say?'

Rose's head turned sharply. 'You'd have to travel there and back every day?'

'It's why I haven't done anything about it,' Lynda answered, standing up. 'I've made up my mind, though. I'm going to risk spending the money on the train fare.' Her mother began to protest. 'I've got to try it, Mother. I'm so desperate for a job.'

Lynda stood at the entrance to a tree-lined drive. The gates were opened wide. It was almost as if they were expecting her. The gates were white, which gave the distant building—Whitegates—its name.

It was useless, she told herself as she neared the large, many-gabled house at the end of the long drive, it had been a wasted journey. Who would want secretarial help in a house such as this? So why had Cormac Daly given her the address?

There was a long wait before there was any kind of response to her pressure on the bell. There was time, she told herself, panicking, to turn and go home, cutting her financial losses. That way, at least she wouldn't have allowed herself to be made a fool of by the unscrupulous head of the company for which she had worked for such a short time.

'Yes?' The door had been opened even as she had begun to plan her escape, and a grey-haired man stood patiently looking at her. Was this the owner of the residence, the person who needed the secretarial assistance and of whom her ex-employer had spoken?

'Oh, I—I've called because I——' she searched her bag and found the slip of paper '—I was given your address. You needed a secretary, or so I was told. But I expect,' she half turned away, 'the position has been filled a long time ago.'

The man shook his head. 'Come in, please, Miss——?'

'Miss Groome,' she supplied. 'Lynda Groome.' As she stepped into the entrance hall, she thought. Even if the job hasn't been filled, what am I doing here?

'I'll take you through if you'll follow me,' the man was saying.

Lynda thanked him, head high, heartbeats speeding, wondering if she really had felt so desperate for a job that she had been so foolish as to come all this way in search of the totally impossible . . .

The man said to the person inside the room, 'There's a young lady to see you, sir.' He backed out, allowing Lynda to pass in front of him.

She heard the door close, felt her weakened limbs grow weaker, her taut fingers tighten around her bag.

'Come in, Miss Groome,' said Cormac Daly like a spider to a fly. 'I've been expecting you.'

There was no welcome in his smile. Not did it touch his eyes. Instead, they raked her figure, coming to rest on her rebellious face.

Lynda felt herself go cold. 'If I'd known who it was,' she flung across at the semi-recumbent figure, 'I wouldn't have wasted my fare money.'

'We're back to the cost of travelling, are we?' She remembered the episode in the studio when he had paid her fare with a careless handful of notes.

'If you offer me money again, Mr Daly, I'll——'

'You won't,' he cut across her threat. 'Nor will you snap at the hand that feeds you.'

'It doesn't any more, Mr Daly.'

His gaze laid a second trail over her, plainly appreciating the way her soft apricot-coloured suit followed the feminine shape beneath it.

'It might, Miss Groome, it just might before the day is out. Take a seat. I'll ask Jack Wendon to organise some coffee.'

'I won't be staying, but thanks for the thought.'

'I said,' the grey eyes slitted, 'take a seat.' Still she held out against him. 'I could make or break you job-wise, Miss Groome.'

'You couldn't. I never give your name to the agencies.'

'So they don't ask what you've been doing with yourself in the intervening weeks between your last stated job and the present time?'

They had and, Lynda thought fiercely, he knew it. She sat down as he had indicated.

'Yes,' he taunted as he watched her resigned movement, 'I thought they might.'

There was a prickling silence and Lynda shifted uncomfortably on the straight-backed chair she had found beside a large, old, paper-strewn table.

'Would you come over here, Miss Groome?' He did not speak imperiously this time. His voice held a note which sounded a chord within her. Not her compassion, she told herself firmly. It was pity that she felt at the way his accident had reduced him. ... Reduced *this* man, she amended her thoughts, a man with his resolute character, his core-deep hardness, his shoulder-span!

Under the open-necked shirt, his chest expanded rhythmically. Lynda felt a near-irresistible urge to put her palms to it and test the strange offer it gave of safe harbour in a storm. She caught at the tail of her leaping thoughts and brought them furiously to heel. Even if this man really did have a job to offer her, she would refuse it. Then she would never need to see him again. Was that what she really wanted?

'I need your help, please.' He regarded her closely, seeing her reluctance to comply and watching her overcome it.

Putting down her bag, she walked across to him and saw that his leg was stretched out stiffly.

'I'll need those.' His head indicated a pair of crutches lying on the floor. 'I can't walk without them.'

She stared down into his face. There was no sign in it of self-pity, only a grim determination to fight at all

costs the disability which made him so reliant on the
help and goodwill of others. His mouth was set, the
curving lines each side of it grooved even more deeply,
she guessed, by his experiences during the weeks since
his accident.

The chord he had disturbed just now reverberated
again, and this time she heard its echo somewhere in the
region of her ribs. A whisper told her it was her pity
again. A tyrant this man might be, but he had asked for
her help and she would give it willingly. She did not
pause to reason why.

'I'll get them,' she answered.

Lifting the crutches from the floor, she stood beside
him. 'Why were they so far away from you?' she asked,
propping them against the table. 'Whoever helped you
in here should have been more thoughtful.'

'I was not helped in here. I only need to be helped to
stand or sit, lie down or get up, plus the other many
variations required by normal living.' No softening of
his features took the edge off the plain statements of
fact.

His hand came out and she put hers in his. Her hand
jerked involuntarily as if she had touched a burning
ember. That chord inside her went mad, and with it
her heart. His eyes were staring at her, but they gave
away nothing. It was his mouth which told her of his
harsh amusement, as if he had guessed what she was
feeling.

His other hand was extended, palm upward. Looking
at it like someone who had been once bitten, Lynda
slowly moved her other hand to rest in his. She was not
holding his hand, he was holding hers! Still he watched
her, but this time she blanked out all feeling from her
expression.

'Now?' she asked, wishing she could hate the touch of
him. He nodded. She pulled, but it was no use—her
strength was unequal to the task required of it. 'I'm
sorry,' she said, trying without success to release her
hands. 'I can't manage it.'

'You'll have to come closer.' The hard smile was

back. He released her at last and lifted his arms, elbows bent. 'Try lifting me here.'

Her hands crept to his armpits, giving him all the support she could manage and her stomach muscles tightened at the intimacy of the action. This time he moved, slowly and upward, nearer to her than he had ever been. Even disabled as he was, he towered above her. She felt the sinewy strength in his arms, saw the breadth of his shoulders.

There was a scent of masculine lotion, a sweep of gritted jaw only a few inches from her cheek, and a chin cleft with determination. She tilted her head and saw that his grey eyes had darkened as they had recorded her increasing awareness of him.

Hurriedly she withdrew her eyes. Her leaping reaction to his nearness troubled her deeply. Without looking at him, she asked, 'If I take my hands away, can you support yourself for a moment?'

He nodded, and she reached out for the crutches. He was taking his weight precariously on his injured leg by holding on to the table. Taking a crutch, he fitted it under one elbow, then repeated the action with the other.

As he started to move, a wince of pain left its mark, then it was gone. Lynda was in his path and she started to move aside, but found it curiously difficult to disentangle herself from the pull of him. They were not touching now, yet it was as if a magnet were dragging her back to him.

I've got to get away from here, she thought. This is madness. I'll never see the man again after this morning. It's all in my mind—it's because I want my job back and I'm secretly pleading with him to revoke his dismissal and reinstate me. . . .

'If you would let me pass?' The icy politeness froze her frenzied thoughts. She side-stepped and he made for the door.

'If it's coffee you want, Mr Daly, I'll find someone.'

'I'll run my own errands, Miss Groome. If I sat in one place all day, I'd put on so much weight that beautiful women like you wouldn't be able to lift me an inch. Nor,' with a satirical sideways glance, 'would they want to come near me.'

Her heart leapt again, responding to the fractional softening of his manner. Following a few paces behind, she heard herself ask, 'Mr Daly, will you give me my job back?' The words had come out of her in a tumbling rush. They had been in her head and she had certainly not intended to speak them . . .

Without turning from his path to the door, he answered, 'No, Miss Groome.' She was left staring at his back, then when that had gone, at nothing. She felt as if he had thrust his fist under her ribs.

'Jack,' she heard him shout, 'we'd like some coffee, Miss Groome and I. Any idea where your wife is?'

'I'll find her, Mr Daly,' came a distant answer.

Cormac Daly swung his crutches round, and he made his slow, teeth-gritting way back to the chair. Lynda stood where he had left her. She still felt stunned—with herself, with the request she had made and with her ex-employer's response to it.

The chair he had come out of had the appearance of an antique. Its back was curved and leather-padded, like the seat. It did not look comfortable, but he stood beside it, looking at her as if waiting for her assistance.

Not again, she thought, her unhappy eyes lifting to his—I can't touch the man again, not after he's slapped me down for the fourth time since I first saw him. That wasn't the reason, that whispering voice told her. It was this frightening effect he had on her. It was tugging her towards him now, even as she struggled to stiffen her legs so as to prevent them from moving.

With a jerk of his head, he instructed her to come round the table to his side. As if he had tugged a string, she did so, taking the crutch he held out, then the other. He stood as if waiting again for her help. She went to him, holding his upper arm, and he lowered himself, stretching out his injured leg as he did so.

A look of tiredness and—could it have been, Lynda

wondered—near-despair passed across his face. She
wanted to rush to him and comfort him. . . . Then,
intercepting her unruly thoughts, she went quickly to
retrieve her handbag. The sooner she could get out of
Cormac Daly's house, the better it would be for her
well-being and peace of mind.

'Nevertheless, Miss Groome,' he said, as if they had
been in the middle of a discussion, 'there's a job on
offer.'

Her heart was responding before her mind had
absorbed what he had said. If only she could tell him,
You know what you can do with your job, don't you?
She sat down, but on the seat's edge. He was observing
her again with that same penetrating look., The hard
curve of his lips implied that he had seen her hesitation.

'When you gave me this address, you mentioned that
secretarial help would be needed,' she said 'How do
you need that when you've got Mrs Peters?'

'As you might have noticed, this is some distance
from London.'

'You mean,' Lynda looked around her, 'you need a
secretary here in your home?'

'I need a secretary wherever I go. In the past, before
this happened,' he touched his injured leg, 'Mrs Peters
did accompany me occasionally to conferences. Her
husband had already begun to object before this,' he
lifted his leg, immediately cursing himself for doing so,
'took me off the ski slopes and into hospital.'

'It must have been a serious fall,' Lynda commented,
hearing the sympathy in her own voice.

'I didn't fall—someone else did. I went after her,
collided with someone who had also gone to her aid,
and I got the worst of it.'

'Her,' he had said. Had it been the 'beautiful female'
to whom Mandy had referred and who had once been
seen hanging on his arm?

'I see,' answered Lynda, since there seemed nothing
else to say. But I don't really see, she thought. Where
was that woman now? 'So,' she went on, since he
remained silent, 'you aren't able to go to conferences

any more. Unless . . .' Just what had he been leading up to?

'Unless my—companion comes with me.'

Lynda frowned. He had made a mistake. 'You mean your secretary. But you've just said Mrs Peters' husband objects, so——'

'I mean,' he cut in, 'my companion. Someone who would be with me in the daytime, helping me as you've just helped me. Someone who'd also be by my side at night, giving me whatever help I might need.'

Lynda found she could not speak. Her heartbeats, already racing, tripped over themselves.

'Am I making the job I have in mind to offer you clear, Miss Groome?' He spoke softly, but his eyes held no gentleness. 'You would no longer lack that commodity you seem to set so much store by, and for which you appear willing to break established rules, not to mention put aside your fastidiousness and good taste to pose——'

'You're insulting me, Mr Daly, and I resent and reject every word you've just said about me. And as for being your companion, whatever that might mean——'

Blandly, he broke into her tirade as if he had not heard a word. 'Tell me the reason for your overpowering desire for money.'

'I don't *desire* it, I need it.'

He sighed, impatient at what he plainly considered her verbal fussiness. Yet he seemed prepared to wait indefinitely for an answer.

A thin, busy woman with greying hair carried in a tray of coffee. She nodded pleasantly to Lynda, who smiled back. 'Here, Mr Daly?' the woman asked, placing the tray on the large table. 'Will the young lady pour?'

'Lynda,' Cormac Daly introduced, 'this is Mrs Wendon. Without her and her husband, this place wouldn't be fit to live in.' The woman laughed. 'Mrs Wendon, Lynda Groome.'

Smiling and nodding, Mrs Wendon went out. Lynda

poured, offering him a cup. He accepted, stirring the coffee and watching her until she was ready to answer his question.

Drinking some coffee, Lynda told him, 'My mother has a small business. It's home-based. For some years, she's hand-knitted garments to order. When my father died, it was the only way she could think of to keep us both.'

'Does she live alone?'

Lynda nodded. 'She started by knitting for friends. They told their friends and it's grown. Now she's developed arthritis in her hands and it's getting more and more painful for her to carry on. The orders are pouring in, but she simply can't keep pace with them, and she's making herself ill with worry.'

Her quick glance upward told her he was entirely impassive, and she watched as he returned his empty cup to the table. Her story, she told herself acidly, had moved his mind, but not his sympathy.

'I don't know what to do,' she went on. 'One of her friends has offered to help her out, taking a share of the money earned.' Lynda sighed. 'My mother feels that if she agrees, and with her hands getting no better, the friend might finish up doing all the work. Then the business would pass out of her control, and she'd be left with nothing.'

'Does she do the work for the love of it?'

'It started off that way. Now she needs to carry on for financial reasons.'

'So what do you intend to do?'

Lynda lifted her shoulders helplessly. 'My mother's having treatment for her hands. All the same, she's losing heart. I think it's not being able to keep up with demand that's affecting her most.' She paused, wondering why she was telling this unfeeling man about her private problems. She added, 'I'm giving her help, paying her bills and so on. But,' she looked at him now, 'without a job, I won't even be able to do that.'

She grew angry with her runaway tongue. Everything she had said was probably being interpreted by her still impassive listener as yet another appeal for reinstatement to her job.

She stood up, saying as briskly as she could manage, 'Thank you for listening. Since there isn't a job at this address,' she pulled out the slip of paper, 'I'll be getting back home.' The paper floated to the floor, and Lynda left it there.

'I told you there was a job on offer.'

She bristled at his sharp tone. 'As your—companion, I think you called it? I've already told you, no thanks.'

'Companion be damned!' he said curtly. 'I want a wife. I'm offering you that position.'

CHAPTER THREE

'You can't be serious!' Lynda sank down again, her knees weak, her eyes staring.

'I've never been more so. I told you, I need physical assistance every day, someone I can call on without wondering how long it will be before an angry husband starts maltreating my body instead of just my ear via the telephone. I need physical assistance at night.' He did not elaborate.

'You must have had that up to now?'

'A hired nurse stays here from late evening to early morning.'

'Why can't you carry on that way?' Lynda heard herself ask. She still had not recovered from the shock of his proposition.

'For the simple reason that I don't choose to. I need a wife. I want a wife.' His eyelids flickered, then stilled. 'I want you as that wife.'

Lynda ran the tip of her tongue over her lips. 'But they said. . . . I was told there's already someone . . . a woman in your life.'

'There was. There isn't now. If there were, I wouldn't be asking you to marry me.'

Lynda shook her head. 'I'm sorry, it can't be done. It's quite impossible.'

'Why? There's a man in your life, is that it?'

Her shoulders lifted and fell. 'John went to work abroad. He asked me to go with him, but I—didn't feel strongly enough about him for that.'

'He wanted you to live with him?'

'At first. Then if it worked out, he intended we should marry. It was all so—so planned, so calculated.'

'What I'm offering you is planned and calculated.'

He was right, every word he had just spoken was true. 'Somehow, it's different.' She had thought aloud.

'How is it different, Lynda?'

The way he had spoken her name, as if it were a caress, made her stare at him. And she knew why it was different—for this man her senses stirred. The way he looked at her sent her mentally reeling. His physique, despite his injury, was that of an athletic man. His brain, she guessed from her few dealings with him, was his driving force. No sooner had he thought, she knew from experience, than he acted.

He had not mentioned the word 'love'. It would have been hypocritical if he had. All the same, there was an indecipherable, niggling feeling of let-down inside her. If only it were possible for her to marry this man and, moreover, marry him for love . . .

'I couldn't possibly marry you, Mr Daly. I told you, it's all too cold, too businesslike.'

'What do you want me to say—that I love you, I can't live without you?'

Yes, yes, she thought, that's what I want . . . 'Of course not,' she answered. 'It couldn't possibly be true.'

'So, I've made you a business proposition,' he continued. 'I'm offering you a job. Without sentiment, an unemotional arrangement which will provide all I need. In return, I intend to provide for all your needs.'

'My needs?' she asked hoarsely, wishing the coffee had not gone cold.

'As my wife, you'll go short of nothing—comfort, clothes, everyday necessities, you won't have to think twice about buying them. I'll also give you a generous allowance.'

Before he had finished speaking, Lynda was shaking her head. 'I couldn't *sell* myself.'

'Isn't that being a little melodramatic? Women these days don't "sell" or even "give" themselves to a man. They're usually considered sharing partners—or,' with a lift of his eyebrows, 'have I got it all wrong?'

'I really don't know,' she answered, hoping she sounded offhand. 'I haven't had the experience of——'

'No experience?' His smile was cynical. 'You surprise me.'

'So I surprise you. I'm sorry, but I'm saying no to your offer.'

'You're also saying no to practical help for your mother.'

'What kind of help for my mother?'

'I don't know where she lives, but do you think it's good enough for her?'

'It certainly isn't,' Lynda replied emphatically.

'Well, there's an empty cottage in the grounds of this house. Accept my proposition and it's hers, plus a generous regular allowance for its upkeep and her own personal requirements. She need never work again, unless she wants to.'

It would, Lynda thought, be a wonderful arrangement, but she exclaimed. 'My mother—you know my weakest spot! It's blackmail you're using, Mr Daly.'

Idly, he rubbed his fingertips over the triangle of hair which was revealed by his partly buttoned shirt. 'Don't use abuse, Lynda, to cover your real inclinations which, I'm perfectly sure, are to accept my offer of marriage.'

He was right about her inclinations, which was why she protested, 'How—how could I enter into an arrangement which is so empty of feeling? I want to marry for love, not expediency.' Her voice had risen, she realised with dismay, and turned her words into a note of appeal.

'If I told you I loved you, would you believe me?'

'Of course not,' she cried. 'How could you love me? How could I——' She had almost said 'love you back'. But I could, she thought, I could so easily fall in love with this man. Look how I want to touch him now, stand near to him again in the way I did when I was helping him to his feet. 'How long would this arrangement——'

'Marriage.'

'This marriage, last?'

'You mean for how long would I tie you to me if you find a man you want to marry for love? Or,' his glance flicked up and then down to his injured leg, 'if I should

find a woman with whom I might become emotionally
involved and wish to marry?'

Why had that last remark hurt so much? she
wondered. She nodded, but his answer was so long in
coming that her hands, already moist, made damp
marks on the soft leather of her handbag.

'I plan to retain your—services as my wife until I no
longer need your personal assistance,' Cormac Daly
told her.

'You mean until you recover completely from your
injury?'

'I mean just that.'

'Do you know how long that might be?' The
answer, she discovered, was suddenly of vital
importance.

'In the next week this plaster will be removed. The
various internal bits of ironmongery—pins and plates
and so on—will stay in for as long as the doctors regard
it as necessary for the bones to knit together. Time
unspecified.'

She nodded, crossing her legs agitatedly and
arranging her skirt with elaborate care. Looking up, she
found he was contemplating her legs with a masculine
detachment. Recrossing them, she found his eyes on her
with an expression that revealed the line his thoughts
had taken—that by the movement she was inviting his
interest.

'It would, of course, be a real marriage,' he added.

A gasp rose to her throat, but she swallowed it. 'In
that case, I don't think——'

'Would you really expect it to be otherwise?'

The quietly spoken question had her confused,
colouring and shaking her head. So now, she thought, I
know exactly what to expect—*if* I say 'yes'. The very
idea of agreeing made her remonstrate again. 'It's all so
cold-blooded! I told you just now, I always wanted—
intended—to marry for love.'

There was something very like pain in the cry, she
could hear it in her own voice.

Slowly, his hand came out. 'Lynda.' He needed her

help again. Putting aside her bag, she went across to him.

'Do you want to stand?' He nodded. Her hands went to his armpits and, with her help, he lifted himself to his feet. His arms came down, trapping her hands where they were. Then she was caught in a hold of iron, catching her to him, compelling her to feel the hard-boned solidity of his body, the pressure of his unencumbered thigh. He pressed her head against his chest, and he cheek felt the rock-like wall there, too.

Now her face was moving of its own accord, rubbing against the soft chest hair, her senses were blind to everything except the fact that she was close, really close, to this man—which, a nameless instinct told her, was where she had wanted to be from the moment she had met him.

He held her away to look into her face, saw what it seemed he had been seeking and moved a hand to the back of her head. Exerting pressure, he brought her mouth towards his, covering the gap with a lowering of his own, and taking control of her parted, quivering lips.

His mouth dismissed the fact that this was the first meeting of their flesh. His lips were hard against her tender mouth and hazily she was aware that the pressure of his kiss was forcing her back. Willingly, she went, knowing instinctively that he would not let her fall.

He did not spare her, plundering her lips until she was gasping for air, clinging to his arms in both fear and ecstasy at the way her body was responding to his mouth's command.

At last he eased her upright, leaving his lips over hers, standing thus until she regained her breath. Her eyes fluttered open and there were his, only eyelash-distant, probing, it seemed, into her very soul. When he released her lips, her head drooped until the top of it found a resting place again against his chest.

'Look at me, Lynda.'

Slowly, she obeyed. His hand found its way through

the opening of her jacket to rest beneath a breast and over her ribs. He was testing the beat of her heart and she knew he would feel its mad throb.

'Now say our marriage will be cold,' he challenged. 'Now tell me our sexual encounters will be devoid of feeling. Tell me now that our every contact will be calculated and mechanical.'

Unable to speak, Lynda shook her head. Her reason struggled to free itself from her emotions. What am I doing here, she reproached herself, in this man's arms? Why have my legs grown so weak that I'm not sure they can hold me much longer? If her emotions were to whisper the answer, she knew her reason wouldn't listen. Yet . . .

All the time she had been thinking, he had been watching her. A passing smile flickered, and he imprisoned her head, more gently this time. 'Will you agree to become my wife?' he asked.

She cleared her dry throat. 'I agree.'

'Without that love you talked about, but by no means devoid of warmth, as we have both just demonstrated?'

'Yes,' she answered, her blue eyes looking into his grey ones to see if the steel had gone away.

'For the financial rewards I'm offering you, and the security I'm prepared to give to your mother?'

The steel had not gone, it was right there glinting down, blinding her and making moisture gather behind her own eyes. She tried to pull away, but his hold tightened.

'No, stay,' he commanded. 'Would you have me be hypocritical, after all, telling you I love you, instead of being honest and restating my reasons for my offer of marriage?'

'No.' She blinked away the tears and indicated again that she wanted him to release her. This time he did so. 'But at least also *re-state*,' her stare accused him, 'that you'll also be getting my constant help. At your side by day, you said, and beside you through the night. That was the bargain.' She tidied her jacket, and smoothed her blouse.

'So the financial side of it is irrelevant?' he taunted.

'That was blackmail on your part. I told you that just now.'

'Stop trying to fool yourself and deceiving me into believing you were entirely altruistic in accepting my proposal. It was only when I offered help for your mother—practical help, involving the expenditure of money—that you overcame your ... let's be kind and call it principles, and agreed to marry me.'

Lynda shook her head, but could not tell him why. It was after he had kissed her, touched her, lighted a fire within her that she had agreed. And it was a fire which, she now knew to her cost, however long their marriage might last and however many years might stretch emptily beyond that, would never be extinguished.

Her eyes were studiedly blank as they lifted to his. 'When does my new—job start, Mr Daly?'

'Right now, Lynda.' His eyes mocked. 'I was named Cormac by my parents. Twist it around your tongue a little and discover how it tastes.'

A smile curved her lips which bore the lingering after-taste of his kisses. 'Cormac.' She frowned. 'It sounds strange to hear myself say it.' Her mind pushed him away like a receding trick television shot, freezing it and turning him into a two-dimensional picture in a company journal.

What was she doing here in his home? Using his given name ... feeling still the imprint of his mouth on hers ... Her mind righted itself from its cartwheel and the reality of the situation gave her all the answers.

She had just agreed to marry the man, hadn't she? By doing so, she had willingly forfeited all right to romantic love, to love of any sort, even affection.

'I like to hear you say it.' He was talking to her and she almost asked him, 'Say what?' His name—from now on she would have to call him Cormac and listen to him calling her by her first name!

'Do I have to? Is it part of the deal?' She had meant to speak sharply, but her mouth insisted on curving upward.

His answering smile was quick to come, quicker to go. 'Take off your jacket. Make yourself at home.' At home, he had said. Had she imagined the faint twist of his mouth?

Cormac took her jacket and, looking round for somewhere within his reach to put it, draped it finally over the table.

He put out a hand. 'My crutches, please.'

Lynda did not respond at once, something inside her objecting to the imperious tone. But she saw his need of help and complied. He hadn't missed her hesitation.

'What's wrong? Don't you like my manner?' He fitted each crutch on to his elbows. 'You'll have to learn to live with it as well as with me—it goes with the job. Will you open the door?'

At the first step, his jaw came out as if he were gritting his teeth. After that, his face was expressionless and he showed no more outward sign of pain. Walking by his side, Lynda looked around her. The hall was large and the wall above a fireplace held a painting which she judged to be of some value. Rugs were scattered over the woodblock floor. The staircase went its curving way upwards to the landing.

Cormac paused by a door and Lynda looked at him. 'This one?' He nodded and she opened it. He eased himself into the room, stopped and waited for Lynda to enter.

Comfort appeared to have been catered for rather than cosmetic impact, and Lynda found the effect pleasing. The ceiling was high, the curtains floor-length, their pattern matching the covered settees and deep chairs arranged around a high-mantelled fireplace designed to suit the time at which the house was built.

Cormac had moved to occupy the settee, his injured leg stretched out, while Lynda sat in one of the armchairs. She felt a creeping coldness inside her at his air of detachment.

'I shall need to know about your family,' Cormac stated.

She stared at the deep blue of the carpet. 'There's

nothing much to tell. You already know my mother's a widow.'

'I should like to meet her.'

Lynda's heart leapt at the implication of Cormac meeting her mother. It made the still unreal situation more of a reality, yet even now she could not completely believe that Cormac Daly had asked her to marry him.

'I—I'll have to ring her first.'

Cormac gestured. 'There's a telephone in the hall, and there's an extension in the room I use at the moment as my bedroom, since I can't walk upstairs.'

'Thanks.' Lynda stood up, smoothing her skirt. 'My mother lives in London, some way from here.'

'I realise that. Mrs Wendon's husband, Jack, will drive us in my car. If it's convenient, make it this afternoon, will you? Around three.'

Lynda's conversation with her mother was selfconscious and short. 'Just a quick visit,' she explained. 'I won't be alone. No, no one you know.'

Returning to the sitting-room, Lynda confirmed the arrangement. Mrs Wendon followed her in. 'How many for lunch, Mr Daly?' she asked, pushing back strands of hair which had strayed out of place.

'Lynda, you'll stay?' It was a question this time, but spoken as though the decision had been made for her. 'Two, Mrs Wendon, please.' As the woman turned, Cormac said casually, 'Miss Groome has agreed to become my wife, Mrs Wendon.'

The woman came to a jerking stop and faced them. 'Have you, dear? I'm delighted to hear it, Mr Daly. If ever a man needed a wife to keep him in order, Miss Groome, it's your young man. You've kept it very dark, Mr Daly, if I may say so. However have you managed to do your courting, with your leg like that?'

Lynda burst out laughing at the once-accepted phrase, and especially at the picture the housekeeper's question conjured up. Even Cormac laughed and Lynda's heart raced at the head thrown back, the painlines banished, the strong, still-tanned throat revealed above the open-necked shirt.

Mrs Wendon wiped her eyes, having joined in the laughter.

Cormac's arm curved invitingly towards Lynda. She went to him at once, unthinkingly, and the arm pulled her down unceremoniously on to his lap.

'Your leg!' she gasped, struggling for other reasons than the one she had just given.

'This is how, Mrs Wendon,' Cormac explained, tipping his captive backwards with one hand and kissing her soundly, making enough noise about it to gladden any sentimentalist's heart.

Mrs Wendon dabbed at her eyes again. 'I bet you didn't stop at that, Mr Daly,' she offered with a touch of impudence, and went out.

There was a small, tight silence which Lynda broke with, 'You can let me go now.'

'Oh, I can, can I? I like the feel of you right where you are. You'll be more—intimate with me before many days have passed. I'll give you ten of them to prepare whatever it is you want to prepare. No more, no less.'

She freed herself from him, confusion colouring her skin at the sensations aroused by his kiss and the pressure of his limbs against hers.

When Mrs Wendon entered the dining-room with the first course, she exclaimed again at the unexpected and, she added, very welcome addition to the family.

'Mrs Wendon comes in daily,' Cormac observed when the housekeeper had gone. 'She cleans and cares for the place as if it were her own. When you move in as my wife, it will be your decision as to what you want her to do that will count, not mine.'

Lynda nodded, hoping her growing responsibilities, domestic as well as business, would be fed to her in small doses. When lunch was over, she walked at Cormac's side to the car. Jack Wendon helped him into the rear seat, while Lynda made for the front passenger door, but Cormac called her back.

'There's room for you beside me,' he said shortly.

Lynda considered the small space left for her beside the strong, tough frame of the man whose fiancée she had miraculously become. He was slewed across the area behind the front seats, his injured leg stretched stiffly.

'There isn't really,' she declared, but Cormac cut in curtly:

'Sit here, Lynda.'

The way he said her name sent a curious flick of feeling through her and she found herself automatically obeying. Jack Wendon looked doubtful, but seemed to translate his employer's insistence on his fiancée's nearness into that of a man who couldn't bear his loved one to be parted from him for the time the journey would take.

Lynda scrambled in, swung her legs to one side and watched as Jack carefully closed the door. They had not gone far when Cormac instructed her to stop fidgeting.

'I'm only trying to get comfortable,' she protested.

'Lift your legs over mine,' he instructed, watching as she did so. The action brought her into a closer entanglement with him, since he deliberately closed his other, uninjured leg to imprison hers. His left hand came out and found a resting place on her thigh.

She looked at him quickly and he smiled at the muted rebellion in her eyes. Thank goodness, she thought, he can't see what he's doing to me inside. Although, she conceded, it probably was not beyond his powers of comprehension to take an inspired guess.

After a few moments, his hand moved a fraction higher. At once, hers came down over his in a self-protective action.

'Please don't,' she whispered, hoping Jack Wendon could not hear.

Cormac's hand did not move, and the only indication he gave of having heard her plea was to curve his lips in a humourless smile as he stared through the window.

All her instincts rebelled, only to alter into an insistent throb of painful longing. He could do this to her with a careless, butterfly-light touch only an hour or so after proposing marriage? Yet she seemed not even to have scratched at the veneer of his feelings.

But was it any wonder, she asked herself, since the arrangement he had suggested to her and her acceptance of it was based on nothing more than a transitory usefulness to him?

And was it only a week or so ago that she had told herself the man was a tyrant, and that she would get him out of her hair if it killed her? Now she had let the man get under her skin to such an extent that a mere glance from him could coil itself around her heart like a lasso! What frightened her most was that something inside her, yet outside her control, was beginning to like it that way.

'We'll stop in town, Jack,' Cormac called to the driver. He gave the name of a nationally-known chain of high-class jewellers, and Jack Wendon raised his hand in acknowledgment.

'Why?' asked Lynda, her eyes wide with disbelief.

'I'll give you one guess,' Cormac answered dryly.

'An engagement ring? There's no need,' she protested.

'Maybe not,' he replied. 'but the world and his wife and kids will need to be impressed by a token of my undying devotion to my beautiful, if eventually expendable, wife-to-be.'

He put out his hand, his fingers moving in a 'put your hand in mine' gesture. Lynda gave a defiant lift of her head and clasped her hands together, catching the corner of his mocking smile as she turned to stare through the car window.

The ring he chose boasted a large diamond, encircled by sapphires. She had tried to reject it, not because she did not like it, because its cost horrified her. Cormac stood there calmly ignoring her protests and signing the slip of paper in payment. He leaned sideways against the counter, while a crutch supported his other side.

He pocketed the two velvet-lined boxes and with Lynda's help, he made for the entrance. Lynda glanced round to thank the woman assistant and caught a look of sympathy on her face, probably prompted by Cormac's stifled curse at the pain the effort inflicted.

'Good luck, madam,' the assistant called, plainly admiring Cormac's physique. 'Happy wedding day!'

Lynda coloured at the woman's envy mingled with pity and lifted her hand in acknowledgment. Cormac did not so much as nod as he excited from the shop.

Waiting for Jack Wendon to appear with the car, Lynda told Cormac, 'My mother expects us about three.'

He nodded with some impatience at being given information he already knew. 'She won't be disappointed. Appreciating disability as I now do, I wouldn't deliberately inflict anxiety on top of anyone else's pain.' He paused, looking with increasing impatience for a sign of his car. 'Is she able to look after herself, or does she need help?'

'She needs help, but——'

'But she can't afford it?'

Lynda nodded, adding, 'I was going to say she won't give in. She fights the arthritis until she's exhausted.' She remembered how, the other day, she had caught her mother unawares, guard down, her face pale, her eyes listless. 'It wears her out, but she keeps struggling to keep up with the orders that come in.' The car was nosing its way towards them through the traffic.

'I'll make sure she gets every comfort.' The car drew up as he glanced her way, catching the gratitude in her glance. 'It's part of the deal, remember?'

The impassive tone was like a blow at her ribs. He's hard, this man I'm pledged to marry, she reminded herself bitterly. Mechanically, she helped him in, climbing into the car beside him. He's offered me marriage without love, passion without feeling. On his side, something inside her said, When the time comes, as it will, for you to give him what he will undoubtedly want, you'll give everything. Look how you feel even now whenever he touches you, looks at you . . .

Jack Wendon, having helped his employer on to the pavement, returned to the car and took out a daily newspaper, folding it to the crossword section. Lynda walked beside Cormac to the wrought-iron garden gate,

holding it open for him, then closing it. He held back to
allow her to go in front of him to the door. Taking out
the key, Lynda found that her hand shook slightly. It
was visible evidence of the state of her nerves. There
was so much news to break to her mother, news that
would shake her small world to its foundations.

'Mum?' she called, cursing the faint tremble in her
voice. 'We're here!' The silence that greeted her
statement made her panic. She was torn between
running to the living-room and staying to help Cormac
manoeuvre his way across the small entrance hall.

Anxiety won, and with a mumbled 'Excuse me' she
hurried to her mother. Rose was seated on the couch,
not a row of knitting in sight, her hands folded neatly
on her lap. Her expression was seraphic, her hair
carefully styled, her outfit the best in her wardrobe.

'Mother, I——'

'Mrs Groome?' Cormac stood in the doorway. His
lightning glance zigzagged from mother to daughter,
lingering on his fiancée. The smile which had started to
spring to the forceful mouth was ripped out by its roots,
and the eyes which had begun to warm turned down to
frozen.

Lynda wondered what she had done to deserve the
blighting censure. She did not know what had
prompted her mother to dress in her best, but she was
delighted that she had done so. If, despite that, Cormac
Daly felt he was lowering himself to impossible social
depths, then as far as she was concerned, the deal was
off.

'Lynda dear,' her mother's questioning gaze urged an
explanation, 'please introduce me to my visitor?'

'I'm—I'm sorry, Mum. This is Cormac—Cormac
Daly. C-Cormac, my mother.' A quick glance told her
she need not have worried about this man's manners,
whether or not he had allocated her and her mother to
a status so low he had decided to call off the coming
marriage.

Her mother repaid the compliment, letting her eyes
dart from her daughter to the man to whom she had

been introduced by his first name. Rose's hand came
out and Lynda saw that she had pushed on to it and the
other hand all of her cherished family rings. Had they
been placed there, she wondered, in an attempt to
disguise the handicap from which the affected fingers
suffered?

It was, as she had discovered, in her mother's nature
always to put the best face on things when it was vital
to do so, even against enormous odds. How her mother
had guessed that this was such an occasion, Lynda
would probably never know. But she could not deny
that she was pleased her mother had been able to sense
that there was something special about this visit. She
had not seen her looking so well for a long time.

Cormac swung across to her, reaching out to take the
proffered hand. He could not have missed the array of
rings even if his eyes had been shut, since he would have
felt them pressing against his palm.

'I'm delighted to meet you, Mrs Groome.' To
Lynda's surprise, he sounded sincere. His smile had
returned—for her mother. When he turned to look
questioningly at Lynda, it had gone again. 'Where shall
I sit?' he asked.

'Oh, anywhere,' answered Lynda, flustered.

'Over there, Mr Daly,' Rose replied, her wits quite
unscattered.

He looked unsmilingly to Lynda for help and she
went at once to take his crutches, lowering him by
holding his upper arms. His glance thanked her, but it
was characteristically mixed with impatience at his own
need for assistance.

'My daughter has mentioned you.' Rose Groome's
opening gambit left Lynda gasping and caused
Cormac's eyebrows to arch.

'No doubt in a derogatory way,' Cormac responded,
smiling and settling back into the years-old chair as if
he belonged. Mrs Groome began to reply but Cormac's
hand silenced her. 'No, don't answer that. I know how
she feels about me.'

Lynda started to colour and told herself it was her

rising annoyance that caused it. 'Do you?' she challenged.

'Should I not know, in the circumstances?' His voice had softened to the level of a secret intimacy.

'I'm so sorry,' Mrs Groome broke in, 'to see you've been injured. Lynda didn't tell me that.'

'It was a skiing accident.' Cormac dismissed the matter.

'The subject just didn't arise, did it, Mother?' Lynda's voice held a faint rebuke, but Mrs Groome just smiled back.

'The last time I saw you—it was three days ago, wasn't it?—you told me you were going after a job at an address you'd been given. Didn't you go after all, dear?' Her eyes widened. 'Oh, and didn't you tell me it was Mr Daly who had given you that address?'

'I did.' Lynda took a seat beside her mother on the settee. 'And guess who I found there, Mum?'

'Mr Daly?' Rose Groome smiled delightedly. 'Now wasn't that kind of him? Especially after sacking you from your job, too.' She frowned. 'Wasn't that an odd way of doing things, though, Mr Daly? I mean, first you sack her, then you get her to go back to you in a roundabout way for a job interview?'

Cormac reached into his pocket, withdrawing one of the small boxes. 'I called her back for this, Mrs Groome.' He flipped open the box and revealed the engagement ring.

CHAPTER FOUR

'LYNDA.'

It was a summons and complying with it went against the grain, but Lynda knew she could not refuse. She perched on the chair arm.

Cormac took her left hand and slipped the ring on to her engagement finger. Then he pulled her down and and placed his mouth on hers. His lips were cold and impersonal. As a betrothal kiss, it made Lynda shiver. Cormac turned to Rose Groome and Lynda perceived that her mother remained puzzled. That kiss, impersonal as it had been, had not fooled her.

'Your daughter has agreed to marry me, Mrs Groome. Can you bear to part with her to my keeping?'

Rose frowned again—it was the frown of a worried parent. 'I still don't understand how all this happened. Lynda seemed to think you were angry with her. She didn't give me any hint that you'd both fallen in love enough to want to marry.'

Cormac pulled Lynda on to his knee as he had done in front of Mrs Wendon. This time there was no noisy kiss to please the sentiments of the onlooker. Instead, he slid his arms under hers, catching her to him, murmuring against her cheek that she should respond in kind.

Her arms needed no instruction from her mind to lift upwards to his neck.

'Give me your mouth,' he whispered, and she obeyed, closing her eyes and loving the feel of his lips on hers. The kiss was so different from the one he had given her a few moments ago, she could scarcely believe it was the same man.

As he lifted his head without letting her go, she stared into his eyes. She was powerless to conceal the pleasure she felt at his closeness, at the flaring warmth between them, no matter how coolly and rationally based his demonstration of 'affection' had been.

Lynda turned her flushed face towards her mother. Cormac still held her and she could find no objection inside herself to the feel of his arms around her.

'Tell me what you think now, Mrs Groome,' Cormac invited with a smile.

'I think,' answered Rose, playing with her rings, 'I think there's deep feeling between you. . . .'

'Oh, there is, Mrs Groome,' Cormac assured her, his smile so dazzling Lynda wondered how much of an effort it had been for him to produce it. 'In our married life, warmth and loving will not be lacking.' He pinched Lynda's chin and she steeled herself not to flinch at the pressure. 'I intend this marriage of ours to work.'

'And me——' Lynda pushed the words at him angrily, but his mouth came at her again, taking yet another kiss. It made her go limp in his arms and left her gazing up at him, her eyes liquid with the love for him which stirred restlessly within her, a love which had come from nowhere and which, she lamented sadly, in the end would have nowhere to go.

'Lynda dear.' Her mother spoke softly and Lynda turned reluctantly to look at her from Cormac's arms. Rose was smiling. 'My mind's at rest now. I don't know how I could ever have thought you would agree to marry a man you didn't truly love.'

Lynda disentangled herself from Cormac and went to sit on a footstool beside her mother. 'I'm glad you're happy about us, Mum. It just happened, didn't it, Cormac?' Her stare dared him to refute her statement.

'It happened just like that, Lynda.' She had never heard his voice so tender. Then she saw the mocking flash of his eyes.

'And it will be a job, Mum,' Lynda went on. 'Being a wife is a job, isn't it? Not only that, I'll be working with Cormac at his office. He needs help there, too. He has a secretary, but I'll be—what will I be, Cormac?' The game was in his court, let him play the ball how he liked.

'My personal—very personal—assistant.' The smile that curved his sensual mouth was at odds with his coolly grey gaze.

Mrs Groome sighed. She seemed delighted with the display of affection.

Cormac was looking around him. 'Are you comfortable here, Mrs Groome?'

'You mean in this flat?' She shook her head. 'The noise at night gets me down. There are young people upstairs, you see. They have friends in, give parties. If I ever need help, they're here before I've stopped calling them—they're wonderful that way—but they aren't my generation. Still,' Rose's shoulders lifted and fell, 'it's my home now. I suppose I'll get used to it eventually.'

'I have a house in the country some thirty miles from London.'

'That address you gave Lynda?'

Cormac nodded.

'There's a cottage in the grounds and it's standing empty. Furnished, of course, but it needs someone living there to keep it warm and dry. I'm offering it to you, Mrs Groome.'

Tears started to Rose's eyes and the beringed hands began to shake. Lynda reached out to cover them with her own. For this happiness, she had agreed to accept the 'job' which Cormac Daly had offered her, the business proposition which necessitated her becoming his wife. Looking at her mother's delight, she knew that the sacrifice of her freedom in agreeing to marry a man who did not love her had been worthwhile.

'You wrung my heart with tales of your mother's poverty and disability. So why did you lie to me?'

They were in the car, crossing London to Lynda's home. Her muscles tautened at his furious accusation and she wanted to throw his ring back at him.

'I didn't lie,' she declared, her anger equalling his. 'Her fingers are stiff and painful, as I told you. She's as short of money as I said she was. What you saw this afternoon was my mother at her best.'

His eyebrows lifted unbelievingly.

'What I'm saying is true,' Lynda declared. 'I caught her the other day as she really is. For the first time since she and I have lived separately after my father died, I didn't phone her to tell her I was coming. I only found out myself that day how she makes a point of dressing in her best, even for me.'

'Was she ill?'

Lynda shook her head. 'Exhausted. Her hands were so painful she couldn't even knit. It's the truth I'm telling you.'

Cormac was silent, staring out of the window. Jack Wendon seemed to have turned diplomatically deaf, appearing not to have heard a word of the exchange. He was driving her home before starting back to Cormac's country house.

Having followed her directions, he drew up outside the house where she lived. Then he got out and wandered round while his passengers talked.

Cormac looked with something like distaste at the hundred-year-old villas which, in their heyday, had plainly housed the financially favoured sections of the population. 'No wonder you've been after as much money as you could get,' he commented cruelly. 'A girl with your physical assets and in your circumstances would obviously use them to their best advantage to improve her standard of living. Chapman probably didn't have to exert much pressure to persuade you to accept his modelling job.'

'Even though it involved my having to break a company rule and lose my job, I suppose,' she retorted.

Her sarcasm rolled off him as he countered, 'Even marrying a man for whom you feel nothing simply because he can offer higher status and as many physical comforts as you could possibly want.'

His comment stung her into hitting out. 'Look, Mr Daly, our marriage was your idea, not mine. I went to the address you gave me for a job——'

'And you got one.'

'A secretarial job——'

'You got that, too.'

'But I didn't bargain for the *job* of looking after you, nursing you, wearing your ring.' She started to tug at it.

'You can back out,' he pointed out. 'We've signed no contract.'

Her struggles with the ring stopped abruptly. She wanted it on her finger, she wanted to be his wife. *She wanted him as her lover and she wanted to be his!*

He watched with a cynical smile her silent acceptance of the situation, the way she unconsciously moved a hand to protect the ring which, a few seconds ago, she had been struggling to remove.

'So once again your acquisitive instincts have prevailed.'

'The last thing I am is acquisitive,' she protested. 'I don't have a longing for material possessions——'

'Only security, comfort and cash in the bank,' Cormac taunted.

'I told you why,' she returned, becoming conscious of the ache around her heart. 'For paying my way, for my mother.'

'Who, from what I've just seen, lives in much better circumstances than you led me to believe, and whose health is nothing like so bad as you described.'

'I told you, you saw her at her best.' Her pain intensified at his intractable attitude, and a glance told her she had not convinced him. She asked dully, 'When does my job start?'

'It's already begun. I shall see to all the formalities prior to the ceremony. It will be a quiet affair—I hope you've no objection?'

'None at all. If I were marrying someone I really loved, I'd want the world to know.'

'For once,' came the dry reply, 'you and I are in complete agreement.' His answer hurt her almost more than she could bear. 'Will you buy the appropriate outfit, the extra clothes you'll need as my wife?'

'I don't think I can——' Lynda checked herself. She had been about to put a weapon in his hand with which to beat her yet again—her need for money.

He was there, all the same. 'Money, is it? Or lack of it.' He sighed exaggeratedly, pulling out his cheque-book, using the hard surface of the plaster on his injured leg to lean on. He wrote on the cheque, signed it and tore it out. 'Don't play the game of refusing, as you usually do, then accepting with false reluctance.'

Her hands clenched, wishing with all her heart that she could refuse.

'Regard this,' he was saying, 'as your personal allowance in advance.'

Still she hesitated. The very act of reaching out for it would be, to her, like sealing a bond.

'I fail to see why you should have any scruples about accepting this amount of money,' he said, 'yet you put up no resistance at all when I pushed that ring on your finger. I can assure you it cost far more than the amount on this cheque.'

How could she explain to him that accepting the ring as an endorsement of their engagement was utterly different from taking money from him? That doing so, in fact, made her feel as though she was selling herself? But, the logic in her argued, wasn't that exactly what she was doing?

'Thank you,' she said tonelessly, taking the piece of paper. 'I'll spend it on a wedding outfit and all the clothes you'll expect a wife of yours to have.'

Cormac made a gesture of irritation. 'Draw up a list of guests you want to invite to the reception, and give me an approximate idea of the number, plus their addresses, of course.'

'Two,' she answered at once. 'My mother and my friend Amanda Ash who used to work beside me in the office.'

'Don't deprive yourself of the pleasure of inviting *all* your friends,' he countered, 'merely because ours will not be a so-called love match.'

'There aren't any others,' she replied in exasperation. 'I'm too out of touch with the various aunts, uncles and cousins in our family. I haven't all your business acquaintances, your high-flown colleagues or your rich friends.'

'I said,' he returned, 'it would be a small affair.'

'Good,' she retorted, 'That's how I shall like it. Anything bigger than small would be a sham.'

'I agree with you,' he answered reasonably, so reasonably she wanted to hit him. 'Press the horn, will you? Jack will come back.'

In reaching past him to the steering wheel, she almost fell across his injured leg. He caught her, brought her down beside him, tipped her face and took a lingering kiss.

Lynda felt herself responding. Horrified, she tried to restrain her clamouring feelings, but it seemed her mouth had developed a will of its own. It clung to his until he pressed his fingers lightly on her cheeks, easing her lips apart. Hers stayed parted, moist and full, revelling in the after-throb. His gaze dwelt on them as if he was wondering whether to slake their apparent thirst.

He said softly. 'You'd better sound the horn, and this time don't trip yourself up deliberately.'

'Deliberately? I——'

He cut through her annoyance and indicated the steering wheel. The blast she gave made all the passers-by turn their heads, let alone Jack Wendon.

Lynda got out of the car while Jack held the door open.

'I'll be in touch,' Cormac called, leaning back, arms folded, with a more than satisfied smile.

Lynda spent the following two days spending the money Cormac had given her.

For the first time in her life, she was able to approach the more expensive stores, knowing there was money in her bank to pay for the quality clothes she had decided to buy.

When she chose her wedding outfit, she intended taking her mother with her, and the outing had been arranged by phone. The allowance which Cormac had

made was considerably more money than Lynda had
ever been used to managing, but she did not even think
twice about taking a taxi across to her mother's part of
London, collecting her and instructing the driver to
take them to the centre of the West End.

Rose Groome asked, as she climbed into the taxi,
'Are you sure, dear?'

Lynda nodded, feeling glad that this, at least, was a
pleasure she had been able to give her mother, a touch
of luxury she had seldom experienced before.

They wandered, light of heart, along Oxford Street,
down Regent Street and back to Bond Street. On the
way, they had made numerous calls into stores, buying
small items which had caught their eyes—Rose with a
self-confessed feeling of guilt, Lynda with an unfamiliar
sense of self-indulgence.

Before choosing her own wedding clothes, Lynda
helped to buy her mother's. It was a powder-blue, silky
two-piece suit with a white embroidered blouse to go
with it. Rose chose white gloves, while Lynda insisted
that she bought a white handbag to match. The shoes
were white, too, and the best quality Rose had ever had.

In the same store, Lynda brought the dress she would
wear for her wedding. It was made of intricately woven
cream lace, with wrist-length sleeves and high-frilled
collar. The lightweight silk jacket was a perfect match.

'I've never seen you look lovelier,' Rose remarked,
her cheeks pink with the day's excitement. 'That dress
fits you perfectly. When Cormac sees you in that, he
won't be able to take his eyes off you!'

He won't even see me, Lynda thought, but made
herself smile at her mother's comment. Looking at her
reflection in the department store's mirror, she saw her
own curving figure and wondered why she had
neglected to reveal it to such advantage in the past.

The weekend went by without a word from Cormac.
In spite of telling herself not to be so foolish, Lynda
fretted and wondered if anything had occurred to make
him change his mind. If it had, she was forced to admit
that she would be the loser in so many ways.

When the phone call finally came, it was from his secretary. 'Mr Daly would like to see you, Miss Groome,' Betty Peters informed Lynda, 'to finalise arrangements, he said. May I say how pleased I was to hear about your forthcoming marriage, Miss Groome? Now, Mr Daly suggested you arrive about ten-fifteen. Will that be convenient for you?'

It was all so businesslike, it made Lynda want to ram the phone down, except that it wasn't Betty Peters' fault.

'It'll suit me fine,' answered Lynda. 'And thanks for your good wishes. I'll see you—and, of course, my fiancé—in an hour's time.'

Exactly an hour later Lynda arrived at the offices of Daly Enterprises. Mick, the doorman, greeted her without a flicker of surprise. Remembering the man's guard dog-like attitude the last time she had called there, Lynda was surprised by his effusive greeting. Had the news of her engagement to Cormac Daly twined itself so quickly around the company's grapevine, or had he been informed for security reasons?

Whatever it was, Lynda received the proffered deference with a pleasant nod and a secret smile. Before leaving home, she had contacted her friend Mandy Ash, arranging for them to meet for a quick coffee in the staff lounge. She knew that at that particular time it would be empty, since it was rarely occupied by any member of staff during working hours.

Mandy had said, 'But I daren't leave my desk, Lynda. It would get me the sack. It's a company rule——'

'Don't worry, Mandy,' Lynda had told her, 'I'll see you won't lose your job.'

'*You* will?' an astonished Mandy had exclaimed.

Lynda took the lift to the fourth floor, reaching the staff lounge as Mandy came round a corner.

'Hi,' said Mandy, giving her friend a quick hug. 'What's all this about? It's lovely to see you again. But how did you get in? I mean, ex-staff aren't allowed back on the premises without special permission from the boss.'

Lynda took two coffees from the vending machine, giving one to Mandy. 'I was especially invited—by the boss,' she explained. 'Mandy,' she sat beside her friend on one of the couches, 'would you believe me if I told you I was engaged?'

'To be married? Who to? Oh, Lynda, that ring!'

'It's beautiful, isn't it? Guess who gave it to me.' Mandy shook her head. 'Cormac Daly! We're to be married in a few days.'

Mandy exclaimed triumphantly, 'I told you it was your looks that caught his attention!'

Lynda laughed, thinking, If only that were true.

'Will you come to the wedding, Mandy?' she asked.

Mandy nodded, seeming too surprised to speak. Lynda told her, diplomatically, how the marriage proposal had come about. She embroidered a little on the facts, concealing the business arrangement angle.

After a chat, Mandy said she would love to attend. 'I'll rush out after work and buy myself an outfit. Let me know the place and time, won't you?' she asked. 'I'm so pleased for you, Lynda. It sounds so romantic.'

'I suppose it was,' Lynda answered, with mock surprise. 'It was certainly sudden.'

Mandy started up. 'I must run. Do I keep this a secret?'

Lynda nodded. 'The others will get to know in time.'

She found Betty Peters in Cormac's room helping him down into his seat as she herself had done at his home. Mrs Peters made a face at Lynda, as if in warning, then she smiled, nodded and hurried out.

'Where the hell have you been?' Cormac growled, and she knew Mrs Peters had been suffering from Cormac's bad mood. 'You got here twenty minutes ago.'

'How do you know?' asked Lynda, frowning. 'I know who it was! Mick, the doorman. He called you on the internal phone and told you I'd arrived.' She thought for a moment. 'Which was probably how you knew that day I came for the photographic session and you came down.'

'He was carrying out instructions.'

'Just as you expect me to carry out yours.'

His eyes narrowed. 'You're so right, my darling.'

His words of endearment made her heart jolt, although he had used them so carelessly. 'Why did you want to see me?' She sat down without waiting to be asked.

The clothes she wore were her old ones—the new outfits she had bought were still packed in their boxes—and it seemed he did not like her simple beige dress with a touch here and there of brown.

'I told you to spend money on yourself,' he growled. 'You look as if you've come for an interview.'

'I did buy new clothes,' she answered heatedly, 'but I refuse to wear anything I've bought with your money until I start the job you've appointed me to.'

His jaw moved forward aggressively. Lynda was sure that if he had been able to move without assistance, he would have come across to her and made her pay for her fighting words.

'The wedding ceremony will be on Friday,' he said sharply. 'I've arranged for the reception to take place at a restaurant not far from where I live. From there, we'll go to my house for the weekend.' He paused and stared with a touch of loathing at his injured leg. 'I don't see what the hell use it is going anywhere else in the circumstances.'

'I'd rather not have a honeymoon, anyway,' she returned quietly. 'It would be different if you loved me.'

'If *I* loved *you*,' he remarked in a curious tone. 'Do I take it that as I don't, the relationship between us is unequal?' He saw her confusion and went on with a devilish gleam, 'In other words, that you love me?'

'I love you?' she was stung to answer. 'How could I love a man who's treated me as you have?' But I do, she thought despairingly, despite his manipulation of my circumstances, in spite of the way he's intending to use me.

'Oh, I have treated you badly!' he returned with deep sarcasm. 'I've given you an extremely valuable ring, plus a large personal allowance. Offered your mother a home near to where her daughter will be living. Offered you marriage and all that that implies. Yes,' he sneered, 'I've treated you abominably, my sweet.'

Another endearment, yet spoken so contemptuously! If only she could hear him speak them with sincerity, with love in his eyes.

It was impossible to argue with any of his statements. Everything he had done since he sacked her had gone to cancel out that harsh act.

Her silence held and she looked up, wondering at his failure to break it. She caught an expression of weariness, as though he was locked in a battle with pain.

As if underlining her thoughts, Cormac said, 'Tomorrow I'm going into a London hospital to have this damned plaster removed. I'll be given exercises to practise by the physiotherapist. I shall still need crutches, but at least I'll be relieved of one discomfort.'

Touched immediately by compassion, she asked, 'Shall I visit you there?'

'That's the last thing I'll want.' Was he hurting her deliberately? He looked her up and down, leaning back in his customary, slightly indolent position. 'I don't like your clothes, but they do nothing to detract from your physical attractions. I doubt if you know what you do to a man. Or am I wrong?'

'I know what the female body does to a man's sexual reflexes,' Lynda retorted.

He burst out laughing, his head going back, the muscles of his throat moving strongly. 'A blunt, not to say clinical reply!' His laughter vanished. 'I deduce from that answer that your unviolated look is quite false.'

She shook her head, but she knew she might just as well have nodded as far as convincing him of her innocence was concerned.

He became brisk and told her the time of the ceremony and the reception and where they would take place. 'A car will be sent for your mother,' he told her. 'Jack Wendon will collect you from your flat.'

Her face was warm as his words brought nearer the moment when she would become his wife. *It will be a real marriage*, he had said. How would she cope with that when the time came, as come it would?

In the intervening days, Lynda packed her belongings into boxes, securing them and pushing them into a corner of the living-room. They were waiting for collection by a removal firm when her possessions would eventually be taken to Cormac's house in the country. What she would do with them once they were there, she couldn't imagine. They certainly wouldn't fit in with the Daly life-style.

Also, they would, in a sense, have belonged to a different person, one whose horizons had been bound by lack of finance, demands of work and modest living conditions. Once she became Cormac Daly's wife, all that would change.

Whether she would like that change remained to be seen, she reflected. Even if she didn't, it would hardly matter, since Cormac had made it clear that even from the beginning, the end of their marriage would be in sight.

Cormac had written to Lynda's mother, telling her that the cottage he had offered her was being refurnished and, where necessary, redecorated. Soon it would be finished and in a fit state for her to move into.

Rose told her daughter on one of her visits what a wonderful man she would be marrying. Lynda thought, but did not say, Cormac's lavish with his money because he has plenty of it. With his emotions and affection, he's mean to the point of miserliness.

Now they were driving back after the reception, and Lynda felt her stomach muscles pulling under the day's strain. Cormac had given her all the moral support she could possibly have needed—she could not fault him on that.

He had played the devoted bridegroom, but his gaze had not once softened as it had swung in her direction. Yet he had stood beside her, making introductions, had

put his arm across her shoulders, and had even kissed
her cheek, to the delight of her mother.

Mandy had come across to her, bright-eyed, saying
she had just met a dishy male who called himself
Cormac's cousin. 'He's asked me for my phone
number!' she chortled, then she had sobered. 'He
doesn't look like a one-girl man. But there's no harm in
dreaming, is there?' she had grinned.

Rose had been assured by Cormac of transport back
to her own place. She had, she told him, begun packing her belongings, but it would be some days before
she was ready to move to the cottage he had promised
her.

Jack Wendon drove slowly, Cormac, at Lynda's side,
had been freed from the plaster around his leg, but it
was bent awkwardly in the rear of the car, and Lynda
felt his continuing pain as her own.

Now and then they glanced at each other. If only he
would say something, she thought. If only I could reach
out and hold his hand, tell him of my feelings for him,
how happy I am despite the shaky base on which our
marriage stands.

He was staring through the window now, and she felt
her lips tremble. If only he would talk about the
weather, she thought, anything rather than this silence.
She wondered what Jack Wendon thought, or did he
imagine they were holding hands?

When the car turned into the entrance drive where
the tall white gates stood open, Lynda felt a sense of
relief. At least, when they arrived, she would be released
from this imprisonment of her body. She would be able
to get away from the morose man at her side. How
many brides, she wondered bitterly, had wanted to
escape from the presence of the man they had just
married?

Jack helped his employer out of the car. Cormac
spoke briefly to his driver, who nodded, smiled in a
kindly way at Lynda, and took the car to the garage.

Cormac opened the front entrance door, standing
back, crutches in place, allowing Lynda to enter. She

stood in the hall, uncertain, feeling a stranger. There was little doubt that she really was.

Cormac swung beside her, his dark suit and pearl-grey shirt and tie adding to his remote air. He hasn't any right to look like this or act like this, she thought, just after our wedding. All right, so I have to accept that he married me for my usefulness to him, but at least he could smile!

With a sweeping gesture, he invited her to precede him into yet another sitting-room. She looked around her, seeing it for the first time. It would take weeks, she felt, to accept that this was her home. It was grander, on a so much larger scale, than she was used to. The two settees were set at right angles to each other, an armchair hugging a corner near to the screened fireplace. The curtains, she noticed, were gold-coloured, going well with the soft-to-the-touch pale brown of the furniture. The carpet on which she stood was a deep-piled fawn.

Flowers had been attractively arranged in every corner, shedding their perfume, lending their colours to lighten the feel of the room. Fresh fruit, piled high, stood on a ceramic dish upon a long, polished coffee table.

'Mrs Wendon has left us a cold meal,' said Cormac, removing his jacket. 'I told her not to come in for the next couple of days.'

'I'm not hungry,' Lynda said, clasping her hands at her waist. 'Did my cases arrive? And my boxes and books?'

'They did. Your clothes are upstairs, and your belongings were put into a storeroom at the rear of the house.' He put aside his crutches and eased himself down on one of the couches. He was more mobile now, able to bend his leg a little, but not as yet allowed to take his weight on it. The removal of the plaster had obviously not relieved him from pain.

He pulled free of his tie and threw it aside, a shadow of weariness darkening his features. Following her instincts, Lynda went to sit beside him. His eyes were closed.

'Is there anything I can get you?' she asked. 'Painkillers? Or a drink?'

'A drink, not painkillers—I'm sick to death of the things. Anyway, I guess I'll need those tonight.' His eyes came open, and an eyebrow lifted sardonically.

Lynda refused to give him the response he demanded. Did he really expect her to flaunt her femininity before him, brashly inviting him to make love?

'A drink?' was all she said.

'Whisky, neat and of the broad Scottish variety. In my present mood, I like its very special flavour.'

She didn't take him up on his allusion to his mood, although she knew he expected it. Swallowing her own private despair, she poured his drink, not knowing the quantity he required. He made no reference to the amount, but tipped back his head and drank.

Returning the glass, he lay back, sighing, his arms stretched along the settee back. Lynda replaced the glass on the silver tray across the room then resuming her seat beside him, she saw that his eyes were half-open, watching her.

'Did I forget,' he murmured, 'to tell you you're beautiful?'

A flare of excitement burned through her and no frantic reasoning in the world could extinguish it, but she answered with commendable coolness, 'Yes, you did.' She smoothed her skirt, knowing his eyes were on her legs. 'But don't let it trouble you.'

'It's no trouble. It's a kind of gratuity, the perks—part of the job you're doing for me as my wife.'

His slitted eyes were on her, his mirthless half-smile prodding at her anger.

'An incentive, maybe,' she hit back, 'to a better performance next time? So that's how a loveless marriage is conducted! You're going to give me a kind of verbal expense account on which I can draw whenever I feel the lack of real affection during our—our *love* making!'

He laughed again, throat moving, white teeth flashing, and Lynda was hit by the sensuality of the man which lurked just beneath the surface. He had, she saw with quick perception, an intense vitality which strained to be let loose, but which had been shackled by his disability.

Her mind reeled at the thought of being in his arms, his injury a thing of the past, joining with him in a joyous union of their bodies and minds.

He had sobered and was looking at her in minute detail, watching the small movement of her breasts as she fought with her latent desires. He reached out and ran a hand over the thrusting curve. At once, she tensed, moving away.

Her action angered him. 'Come here,' he ordered. 'You know my movements are limited.'

She stood up, quite out of his reach. 'I'd like to change. Where is my room, please?'

'Don't be so damned formal. You're my wife.'

Lynda did not answer, waiting for him to tell her where to find her cases. She tried again, 'Are you still sleeping downstairs?'

'*We* are sleeping upstairs. There's an adjoining room with cupboards, a dressing-table. There's also an en suite bathroom.'

'Are you able to manage the stairs now?' She looked at his left leg, which was partly bent, yet still half-stretched out as if his muscles had not yet grown used to their freedom.

'I am. It's no picnic climbing them, even with crutches, but I manage in my fashion.'

'Where's the room I—we—are going to use?'

'Turn right at the top of the stairs. Two doors along.'

The moment she reached the hall, she began to shiver. His eyes, she knew, had not left her as she had walked to the door. It's our wedding day, her brain reminded her repeatedly as she climbed the stairs. We should be laughing, loving ... What have I ever done to make him behave like this towards me?

The earlier flare of excitement had been doused by the calculated indifference of his manner. She entered the bedroom with a feeling of apprehension, but the impact of its furnishings, fitted wardrobes and mirrors, the pale blue carpet made her forget her underlying anxiety with an appreciation of the room's tastefulness.

A partly-opened door led her to a bathroom complete with shower cabinet. Another door on the opposite side of the room opened into a reasonably-sized dressing-room. Cormac had mentioned everything it contained except the bed.

Lynda hurried back into the main room, took her cases which had been placed to one side and carried them into the smaller room. This, she decided, would be hers, here her clothes would be hung and here she would sleep.

After a hurried shower, the dress she chose to wear was a high-necked sleeveless shirtwaister in varied pastel colours. It was caught at the waist by a rope belt, and she fastened on a shell choker necklace. Slipping on white sandals, she flicked back her hair with a comb and fixed a little make-up over her slightly flushed cheeks.

The excitement she had felt earlier had rekindled, and again she found it impossible to talk it out of her system. Cormac was her husband now, and even though it might not be for ever, she would live in the present and make the most of the way her life had changed.

Opening the living-room door, she found Cormac exactly where she had left him. He had opened the neck of his shirt, and one of his arms was still spread along the settee back, while the other was lifted to support his head.

As he looked at her, a curious expression flitted across his face, but all he said was, 'I admire your taste in clothes.'

Lynda nodded without smiling, asking, 'Would you like me to serve the meal now?' She had to hold back the rush of feeling at the sight of his broad, muscular, lazy-seeming body.

He appeared to give the matter some thought, all the while letting his eyes scan her shape. 'Yes, I would like,' he answered at last, a faint lift to his mouth.

Now she felt a rush, not of excitement, but of anger, and she was sure he had guessed. 'Would you please tell me where the dining-room is?'

He waved an arm vaguely. 'The room next to this. Make it informal.'

She took a breath, expelled it and blurted out, 'I'd like to throw it at you!'

Once more she heard his laughter, mocking this time. He knew what he was doing to her!

Mrs Wendon had left a quiche, another savoury flan and an assortment of salads. She had left a note suggesting that for a sweet, they might like the lemon mousse she had made, or ice cream and chocolate sauce. The coffee, Lynda read, was all measured out in the coffee machine and all she had to do was to switch it on.

Lynda thanked goodness for Mrs Wendon and set about preparing the meal. The dining-table, she discovered, had already been set—very formally, despite Cormac's instructions. She shrugged, and carried on.

Returning to the sitting-room, she found that he had changed position slightly and that his head was back, eyes closed, while a frown pleated his broad brow.

'Are you in pain?' she asked quickly.

His eyes came open and he seemed surprised. 'Where did you learn your ability to mind-read?' He shifted, moving forward. 'The answer is that I am. But I should be used to it by now. Will you come and help me?'

He watched her approaching and took her hand as it came towards him. 'Give me your other hand, too,' he directed, and she did.

Exerting all her strength, she pulled him up and gave him his crutches. He cursed them, but swung after her, inclining his head as she opened the door and stood back for him.

He stayed in the dining-room doorway, then gestured to the highly-polished dark oak table, around which were grouped matching upright chairs. There were two place settings, each with crystal glasses and shining silver cutlery. Flowers, in a green glass vase, occupied the central position.

'I said make it informal.'

Lynda took exception to his curtness. 'It was already set like this—I wouldn't have bothered. Mrs Wendon must have thought we had something to celebrate.'

His eyes burned fire at her. It was like the look he had given her across the open-plan office the first time she had seen him. 'Leave the sarcasm to me. Maybe *I* have something to celebrate—the acquisition of a tame and willing wife, ready at any moment to do my bidding.'

She had no answer to his deliberate insult. Expressionlessly, she asked. 'Do you require help with seating yourself?'

'Yes.' He neared the chair at the head of the table, handing her his crutches. She helped him ease down and he thanked her with a nod.

'I hope the food provided pleases you,' she commented, taking her place at the other end of the table. 'It was, as you told me, left by Mrs Wendon.'

'For God's sake, move nearer this end. How can we carry on a conversation with you up there?'

'By telephone,' she remarked, the idea making her smile. 'Or we could throw notes at each other?' She sat in the centre of one of the sides, moving her place setting.

'I have it from source that you'd like to throw more than notes at me.'

Lynda glanced at him, smiling, and caught a strange look which turned her heart over. She inhaled a breath, catching the scent of the flowers mixed with the appetising aroma of the food. 'Can I help you,' she gestured to the various dishes, 'or can you manage?'

'I can manage, my thoughtful bride,' he returned with sarcasm, making her colour at the endearment and the term he had used. But her smile died away when he added, 'I don't need to be fed. It's my leg, not my arm that has been injured.'

'I only asked,' she blurted out, half pushing back her chair. 'I really thought you might like help.' Feeling tears well, she made for the door.

'Come back!' called Cormac, half-turning in his seat.

'I'm not hungry. I've lost my appetite.' Her voice was thick despite her effort to clear it.

Running up the stairs, she went through the main bedroom to the smaller room. She threw herself on to the bed, rumpling the cover, rolling her head against its softness. He would not reduce her to tears! When she agreed to marry him, she knew what she was taking on, didn't she?

All the same, she hadn't really expected this terrible anti-climax. She had expected to be treated at least with respect. There's a terrible gap between us, she thought, sitting up and smoothing her hair. I still look on him as an employer. Yet—a terror gripped her—he's my *husband*. How could that chasm ever be crossed?

CHAPTER FIVE

FOR some time she stayed in the dressing-room. After a while, she unpacked one of her suitcases, hanging her dresses and jackets in the wall cupboards. Then she wandered back into the main bedroom, staring at the large bed, seeing the door mirrors, noting the brown leather couch along a wall with cushions and a couple of sheepskin rugs thrown across the arms.

On a small circular table stood an arrangement of flowers. Beside it was a framed photograph of a woman.

She was half reclining on a couch, the couch in that room. Her hair was golden and combed backwards from her forehead. Giant gold earrings glinted beside a face which tapered from high cheekbones to chin. Gold jersey swathed her curvaceous body, high-heeled matching sandals peeped from the draped hemline.

Eyes looked askance at the photographer, provocative and knowing. There was sensuality in the beautiful face, but nothing to put a light to the personality. Lynda considered the portrait. There probably was, as the picture showed, no depth in the woman's character to illuminate.

Telling herself she couldn't lurk upstairs until nightfall, Lynda went quietly on to the landing, looking left and right, following the beige carpeting edging the numerous doorways. Had Cormac shared the place with that woman? How often had she shared his bed? And where was she now?

Cormac was still at the table. He had eaten his first course—hers remained where she had left it. His eyes were on her again, but this time inspecting her face.

Was he looking for a trace of tears? Well, Lynda thought, he's looking in vain. I cried inside, not

82

outwardly. I refuse to let him see how much he's
hurting me.

'So you didn't run out on me,' he taunted as she took
her place at the table. 'I thought I might find myself in
the divorce court before I'd got you into bed for our
first night of *love* making.' He mocked her own earlier
emphasis.

Forcing herself to stay calm, she answered, starting
on her meal, 'I married you to help you in every way I
can, and I'll do everything within my power to do just
that. I'll do anything but sleep with you.' She swallowed
a mouthful and, with it, her apprehension about his
response.

He did not react at all. He merely watched her as she
ate, but she refused to allow his unsmiling scrutiny to
diminish her appetite. In the end, she had to force
herself to clear her plate. Rising, she said, 'I'll get the
sweet. Would you like mousse or ice cream?'

'If it's Mrs Wendon's, I'll have the mousse.'

She nodded, taking the empty dishes. 'Coffee?' she
asked, keeping her eyes dull and her voice expressionless.

He nodded. 'Black. We'll have it in the sitting-room.'

The mousse was delicious, but Lynda could not
appreciate the subtlety of its flavour. The deep silence
did nothing for her taste buds. Noting that Cormac had
finished, she rose to collect the dishes.

'There's a dishwasher,' Cormac informed her as she
moved round the table.

'I had noticed, thank you.'

The look with which she was growing familiar sliced
through her again. Going into the kitchen, she filled the
machine and returned to clear the table. A hand shot
out, catching her wrist.

'I didn't marry you for you to act like a bloody
waitress!'

Lynda tried to free her wrist, but the action hurt
almost as much as his grip. Her lip began to tremble,
but she hid the movement by saying, 'Didn't you? I
thought I was acting the perfect housewife.'

His grip tightened and his jaw moved. 'Leave the sarcasm to me, I said.'

'Did you? How else am I going to fight you?' she blazed.

'I'll tell you how.' He jerked her on to his lap and she found herself pressed helplessly between the table edge and the wall of his body. She was afraid to move. If she did, she knew she would either hurt herself or his leg.

'Let me go, Cormac,' she urged, but he ignored her plea.

His palm imprisoned her head, his other hand fastened on her upper arm. 'Fight me now,' he said, and brought his mouth down on her parted lips. Her self-respect urged her to resist. He's only using you, it said, but it lost the battle against his powerful weapons.

His mouth was hard and abrasive against the inner moistness of hers. Her hand on his shoulder stopped pushing at it and held on as his hand moved. Her head was going backwards, tasting the fire with which he was consuming her mouth. His hand had found its way through to her breast and even that had begun to burn under his stroking touch. Her fingers crept up his neck to rub frantically through his hair. The table was pressing into her, but she didn't even notice the pain.

At last he eased her upright and her hands dropped to his shoulders. He released her head, but his hold on her breast remained. It throbbed under his moulding pressure and her head went forward to rest against his chest.

'Why didn't you fight me?' His voice had lost its edge. There was a strange note in it that made Lynda look at him.

'I—I couldn't. I might have——' she searched for a plausible reason '—hurt your leg.'

'You're hurting it just by sitting on it.' His hand covered her mouth. 'I know what you're going to say—I put you there. I can tell you now,' his eyes glittered like an icicle in the sunlight, 'it was worth the pain.'

Her eyes roved over his face, seeing in close-up the marks that time and experience had placed there. His chin's cleft was deep, his lips full of resolution and demand. She wanted to rub away the cynical groove from nose to jawline.

'Touch me,' he invited, and the words held an invitation she wanted desperately to accept.

She shook her head, struggling to rise. Cormac let her go and she saw the frown of pain as her weight left him. Her instinct was to reach out and try to ease the discomfort she had caused, but he must have interpreted her look as pity, because he waved her away.

There was a sound from the kitchen indicating that the coffee was ready. Still feeling the impression of his mouth, the warmth his intimate touch had begun to arouse, Lynda returned to the kitchen. Taking the coffee tray into the sitting-room, Lynda went back to Cormac.

He sat at the table like a trapped animal snarling at its enforced immobility. She felt the strength of his fury raying out towards her, but she did not hesitate to go to him. He snatched each crutch from her and plainly resented her outstretched helping hands.

She stood aside to let him pass, but he motioned her on in front of him. After helping him to his seat on the settee, she poured the coffee and gave him a cup. He nodded and drank, then put his head back to rest.

Watching him, Lynda drank her coffee, wondering whether he would let her do anything to help him. His eyes came open and he saw her compassion.

'I'm sick of you looking at me like that,' he threw at her and took a gulp of coffee. 'So I'm in pain—okay, I accept it, and it's about time you accepted the fact. That's why I married you—to give me physical help whenever I need it, not to stare at me pityingly with those baby-blue eyes!'

Lynda compressed her lips and jerked to her feet, collecting the cups. 'Since there's nothing I can say or do that pleases you,' she said coldly, 'I'll get out of your way. If you hate having me around as much as you seem to do,' she steadied her voice, which to her annoyance had wavered, 'I'll pack up and leave and the marriage can be annulled.'

His eyes snapped. 'Do that, my darling wife, and your mother will lose her new home. You'll have to find another, too, since you've given up your old one. Nor will you have a job, and as I said before, I'll make damned sure you won't get another for a very long time!'

She dropped the tray back on to the coffee table and the cups rattled madly. 'You make me sick!' she cried. 'I wish I'd never come here that day and taken that *job* you offered me. I wish I'd never met you!'

She ran out of the room, looking first one way, then another. Where could she go to get away from him? The garden beckoned and she made for the kitchen, finding the back door and wrenching it open.

The evening air was cool and she shivered, but did not turn back. There was a side entrance to the near garden, and she opened the gate to find a paved way stretching outward from the house. There were flower-filled beds in low-built walls bordering the area. Steps led down on to lawn and shrubs and opening out beyond that, a miniature parkland with trees spreading their branches at wide intervals.

The grounds were much larger than she had even guessed. Beyond them was a view of fields and distant wooded hills. Lynda wanted to fling her arms wide and run free, away—away from the building which held the tormenting, bad-tempered man for whom, deep within her, an irrational feeling had developed and grown from her first sight of him. Now, the roots of her loving were so strong, she was aware of how much she would suffer when the time came, as come it would—hadn't he warned her?—for them to be torn out and thrown aside.

Re-entering the house, she made her way upstairs. She did not know whether Cormac could manage to get himself up from the settee, but at that moment she had no wish to go near him. After his nastiness and his threats, she told herself, she didn't care if he had to sleep there all night!

After undressing and washing, she closed the communicating door firmly and got into the small double bed. Pulling the cover over her, she lay there, staring at the half-pulled curtains and watching a semi-circle of moon rise into her line of vision.

All right, she told herself, as the piece of moon blurred and floated, it was her wedding night. But she had never expected anything of it. How could she? Anyway, if Cormac had wanted to make love to her she would have hated every moment in his arms.

Shivering slightly, she lay there listening to the country silence, waiting for the sleep that wouldn't come. Her body stiffened as her ears told her of sounds on the other side of the door. There was a line of light underneath it. Cormac had managed the stairs and come to bed!

Her fists clenched at her sides, her feet curled, waiting for the moment when he would stomp in and demand that she share his bed. The sounds went on, the slow thump of crutches, the opening of another door and the rush of water. Was he taking a shower unaided? Her instinct to help was alerted, but she stayed where she was.

It seemed he had managed without anyone's assistance. Still Lynda listened, for the sounds of a man settling down, for the return of the silence. Suddenly her door was thrown open, and the light switched on, blinding her.

'My room is yours. My bed is yours.' There was menace in his voice, anger in his eyes. 'Come, join me there.'

Lynda took her hand from her eyes, accustomed now to the light. But not to the presence of her husband. He wore a robe, loosely tied. His height and breadth drew her like a magnet, but she spat, 'I told you I'd do anything for you except——'

'Sleep with me you will!'

She half sat up, battle in her stare. 'How will you make me?'

'Don't taunt me, or tempt me, sweetheart. My leg

may be injured, but in all other respects I function normally as a man.'

Her skin began to prickle, knowing she could not push him much farther without his retaliation taking its toll of her. A powerful weapon was a barrage of words. It was all she had, really, so she began to use them.

'Is this phase two of my marriage contract with you?' she attacked. 'I've successfully completed phase one—the perfect housewife. Now I suppose I have to fulfil the next stage, performing the marital ritual, giving you dominance over my body.' She ignored the fire in his eyes. 'After that—I'm guessing—comes supremacy over my mind.'

He towered over the bed, supporting himself on his uninjured leg and one crutch, while he rested the other support against the bedside table. He reached down and pulled the cover from her, then he gripped her upper arm, his fingertips sinking in. He pulled and tugged until she was almost off the bed.

Afraid that her resistance might add to the injury of his damaged leg, Lynda swung herself round and her feet found the floor. His arm thrust round her small waist and through the filmy material of her nightdress she felt the singeing warmth of his body as his robe rayed open below its tie-belt. She had never been so close to a man and the pressure against her of his arousal stirred a responding, questing heat inside her.

His mouth conducted a ruthless depth-probe of hers, pressing back her head until she cried out, but no sound came. He was easing away the straps of her nightdress until it fell at her feet and she stood naked before him. He gave her a scorching look, tipping her backwards until she fell on to the bed. The remaining crutch fell away, then he was stretched beside her, his palm running over her, his robe discarded and she felt the residue of moisture from his shower. He paused, lifting his head, his hand on her stomach. His eyes were lit from within, an angry kind of hunger in them.

'Make love to me, lovely,' he demanded. 'Show me everything you know.'

Her head moved negatively on the pillow. 'I don't know,' she whispered. 'I don't know.' There was a glow in her gaze and leaping expectation. 'Teach me, Cormac, show me how.'

The light in his eyes went out and the anger in his hunger took hold. 'I'll teach you,' he rasped. 'I'll show you how. If I hurt you,' he said through his teeth, 'then you'll know how I'm feeling.'

His hand became a pathfinder, discovering places that made her arch and writhe until she cried out her need. He moved on to her and even in her passion-clouded state, she caught his wince of pain. Then she felt the thrust of him and the pain he had promised. Even so, the sensation was such that she never wanted it to stop, but stop it did—it was over too soon.

Cormac lay against her, his head on the pillow, and she ran her hands over the strength of his back. It was a new discovery and she delighted in it, but he moved irritably to make her stop. It seemed he could not stand her touch.

He pulled away and the separation held a possessive intimacy all its own. Then he rolled from her and she saw his face.

'What's wrong,' she whispered, 'what's wrong? I belong to you now.' She did not understand why he was so angry. 'I told you. I told you,' she repeated, dismayed, 'when you first proposed our marriage, I said I was inexperienced. Surely you understood what I meant?'

His feet swung to the floor and he pulled on his robe. 'Inexperience can mean a lot of things. It's plain I interpreted it the wrong way.' He turned on her and she curled up into herself on her side. 'How do you expect a man in my state,' his eyes ravaged her, 'to teach you how to make love?'

His question made her sick at heart. 'Would you have preferred it,' she said wildly, 'if I'd had a dozen men and received their varied tutelage? If I had, how do you know I wouldn't have criticised your lovemaking?'

'So criticise,' he snapped viciously. 'I'm accustomed

to give and take in loveplay, not give, receiving
nothing.'

'Receiving nothing?' she cried, bewildered. 'What
have I just given you, but everything I have to give?'

He took hold of his crutches and went from the
room. The slam of the door made her head reverberate
with his hatred.

'Lynda.' Her name drifted into her dream, making
her stir and turn on to her back. 'Lynda!' It came at her
again, and this time she knew it was not part of her
dream and uttered by a lover as a caress, but was a
command from the man who was paying her to act as
his wife.

For a moment she did not move, wondering where
she was. Then the memories began to return. Her
dreams might have been sweet, she thought, but reality
was stark.

'Lynda, I need your help!' It came as an order, not a
request. All the same, she could not resist the demand,
curt though it had been.

She pulled on her wrap and opened the door. Cormac
was seated on the side of the bed. He was dressed in a
navy open-necked shirt and slacks, and wore a weekend
look. One shoe was on, the other in his hand.

Lynda had had no time to feel embarrassed at their
meeting again after the events of the night, but now a
strange selfconsciousness swept her as he looked at her
rumpled hair and flimsy nightclothes. There was an
unmistakable reminiscence in his eyes, but he did not
greet her, nor did he smile, and Lynda felt this most of
all.

'Did you want me?' she asked, feeling like a dutiful
employee.

'Would I have shouted if I hadn't?'

Steeling herself to ignore his brusqueness, she saw
why he had called for her assistance. Crossing to him,
she took his shoe and fitted it on to his foot. 'How have
you managed before?' she asked, straightening.

'I told you, I had a night nurse. Now that damned
plaster's off my leg, I'm only fractionally more mobile.'

'So now you've swopped a nurse for a wife,' Lynda commented, pulling her wrap more tightly about her. 'Did she sleep where I'm sleeping?' she asked sweetly.

He flashed her a dry look. 'I told you, I slept downstairs,' he answered. 'And in any case, she was a middle-aged lady.'

Lynda could not suppress a smile. He caught it, picked up its infectious quality and curved his own mouth in response.

He indicated that he wanted to stand and she saw that his crutches had fallen out of his reach. She picked them up, helping him to his feet. In a second, his arms were round her and she felt the length of him pressing into her soft flesh.

'I was a fool to get dressed,' he said thickly, his hand moving from her shoulders down to the small of her back. 'I could take you now. Look at your eyes,' his finger traced a line under them, 'still bright from my initiations of you into the ritual of intimacy between lovers.'

His palm had moved lower, rekindling her desire. 'Ritual, you call it?' she challenged, the nerves of her skin leaping under the feather-touch of his knowing hand. 'Is that all lovemaking means to you? A purely physical thing?'

'Give me another name for it,' he encouraged, his eyes all over her. 'It's a primitive, driving need. It has to be, otherwise the species would have died out.'

Lynda pulled from him irritably. He was taking the colour out of her day. Deliberate though his possession of her had been the night before, the sun still shone brighter, the birds sang more sweetly because of their coming together.

Going to the door, she said, 'I'm getting dressed. Mind if I have a shower?'

'Help yourself. If I weren't incapacitated, I'd join you.'

Ignoring the sensual flicker in his eyes, she asked, 'What do you have for breakfast?'

'Whatever's put in front of me. Can you cook?'

The question seemed so comical coming from the man she had married the day before that she laughed, her hair flying back. 'What else would you like to know about me? Can I drive, can I swim, can I stand on my head?'

'We must get together some time,' he remarked with a half-smile. 'We might get to know each other a little better—on the purely mental level, of course.'

His gaze moved slowly down to her thighs, which she knew would be visible under the see-through nightwear.

Lynda pointed to the photograph of the voluptuous woman on the table. 'As well as you know her?'

His smile vanished without trace. She decided it would be best to dodge his anger and scurried back to the dressing-room.

The day limped by and Lynda wondered whether the accord they had been on the edge of achieving that morning would ever return.

Wandering round, she opened doors, finding rooms she hadn't known existed. There was another living-room, the breakfast room they had used that morning, and a further room whose walls were lined with books. Someone, probably Cormac, seemed intent on building up a library. Yet another room held hi-fi equipment and another television set.

Wandering to the window, she wondered where Cormac had gone. After lunch, he had left her in the kitchen, telling her to do whatever she wanted.

'Can you drive?' he queried, and when she had nodded, he told her there was a car in the garage. 'Go for a drive,' he had said offhandedly. 'Look at the countryside.'

'Couldn't you come with me?' she had asked, pleading like a small child for a sweet.

He had looked at her, scanning her short-sleeved checked blouse and jeans, making her wish she had dressed with just a little more femininity, if only to take that mocking look off his face.

'No, thanks,' he said shortly. 'I've seen it all before.'

Lynda had sighed and turned away. 'It won't be any fun on my own.' If she had hoped he would change his mind with her sad little comment, then she would have been disappointed. He had merely walked off, saying nothing.

Now, she stared through the window at the gardens, flower colours bright in the afternoon sun. There was the distant ring of the telephone and thinking it might be her mother, Lynda raced along the entrance hall, making for the telephone table which was set in an alcove, and picked up the receiver.

'Hi,' said a male voice. 'Cormac?'

It took Lynda a few seconds to collect her wits. Where had she heard that voice before? There had been so many other voices. ... Yesterday, at the wedding reception!

'Who's there, then?' the voice asked, as if puzzled. 'Mrs Wendon?' A pause. 'Or the new Mrs Daly?'

'Right third time,' answered Lynda, smiling.

'Oh, hi!' the voice said with heightened interest. 'This is Rodge—Rodge Miller. No, not Roger,' as if he were used to correcting people, 'Rodge, R-O-D-G-E,' he spelt it clearly. 'Derivation distinctly olde-worlde, Middle Ages or something. Remember me from yesterday? I'm Cormac's cousin.'

The man Mandy had called dishy, and who had taken her telephone number!

'We didn't actually meet,' said Lynda.

'What the hell do you want, Rodge?' Cormac's voice broke in, making it a three-way conversation.

'Snatched the phone from your wife's hand, Cormac?' Rodge joked.

'No, I'm on the study extension.'

'Is that where you've been?' Lynda asked indignantly.

'You don't mean you've actually been working today?' the caller asked incredulously. 'I'd have thought you'd have better things to do. If I'd been in your shoes——'

'I doubt if marriage figures very highly, Rodge, on

your list of life's essentials,' Cormac said with acerbity. 'Why did you ring?'

It can wait, thanks,' Rodge answered. 'Any objections if I come over and keep your wife company?'

'Plenty. But when I suggested she might take a look at the surrounding countryside, she seemed to want her hand held. It would relieve my conscience if you complied with her wishes.'

The extension phone slammed down and Lynda drew in her breath.

'Wow! Have you two quarrelled?' asked Rodge. 'If you have, don't let me interrupt. They say that whoever tries to separate two fighting dogs usually gets bitten himself, so maybe I'd better stay away.'

'We haven't quarrelled, it's just Cormac's way. I mean . . .'

'You mean he was born like it. I can assure you he wasn't. It was that b—— Sorry, Lynda. I'll come round if you want me to.'

'Yes, please. Do you live far away?'

'My own place is in London. This weekend I came to my parents' house for the wedding—your wedding. It's about twenty minutes by car. Give me half an hour.'

Lynda hurried upstairs and changed into a salmon-pink blouse and cream-coloured skirt. She applied make-up and brushed her hair until it crackled, then fixed earrings. It was a defiant gesture, and if Cormac took it as her way of expressing her wish to be more attractive to his cousin than to himself, then she told herself she did not care.

She raced down the stairs, knocked once on the door of Cormac's study and went in. 'Why are you so unpleasant to me?' she exploded, standing in the doorway. 'Did you have to be so nasty about me just now on the phone? What have I done to you to make you like that?' Her voice had risen and she had only just managed to control its waver.

He put down his pen and leaned back. 'Married me for money,' he answered flatly.

How little you know, she thought with a lump in her throat, but answered, 'Believe that if you like, but you're getting your money's worth, you have to admit that. You're getting my help whenever you want it, you're getting . . . me.'

'Yes, I am, aren't I?' His eyes flickered, turning sensual as they looked her over. 'Come here, my love.' There was cynicism even in the endearment, but Lynda could not bring herself to resist the command.

Didn't she want to touch the man who had made love to her last night? Didn't she want him to rekindle the fire, throwing kisses on her like fuel to feed the flames? When she stood by his side as he sat alongside the table, his injured leg stretched out, she stared down into his fathomless grey eyes. He must have mesmerised her and broken down her ingrained barriers, since she found that her hand was stroking his shoulders.

In less than a second, she was twisted round and on his knee and wrapped around in arms of steel. He was kissing her, soaking her into him as if trying to drain her of her life force so that she would have nothing left for any other man who might try and take her.

When he lifted his head, his hand, which had made a place for itself on her breast, having unfastened the buttons, stayed where it was, but tightened in its hold. He looked down into her flushed face, at her full, pulsating lips.

'You dressed up for my cousin, but didn't give a damn about me!'

Lynda could only stare back at him, throbbing with the ache of desire he was arousing by the circular movement of his thumb. Then it was over and he was pushing her from his lap.

Her colour high with the heat of unfulfilled longing, she fastened the buttons one by one. 'If you'd stayed with me instead of hiding yourself away,' she muttered, 'I would have changed. We could have gone somewhere . . .'

'You've got a playmate coming,' Cormac said curtly. 'He'll be here soon. He can't resist an attractive woman.

But if he tries once to overstep the limits with you, I personally will throw him out.'

'Do you really think I'm the sort that would let him?'

'I know why you married me. Since I've only got that as a criterion, I have every reason to believe that you might well be "that sort".'

'You don't really know why I married you,' she retorted from the door.

His mouth assumed a broad grin. 'Because you love me? Tell that to the trees!' With that, he returned to his work.

Rodge was fair, tall and smiling. He looked Lynda over with appreciation and there was nothing there to which she could take exception.

'Cormac's tastes have changed,' Rodge commented. 'A great improvement, too. More in line with mine.' He put his head on one side. 'You wouldn't do a swop? Him for me?' He gestured towards the study, the door of which was partly open.

'This soon?' Lynda joked. 'Our marriage is hardly tried and tested. Ask me again in three months!'

There was a crashing thump from the study along the hall.

Rodge grinned, raising his voice. 'There must be something wrong with my cousin. If I'd married you yesterday, I'd have had you in bed with me——'

'Rodge!' A roar came from the half-opened door. 'Find a woman of your own. The one you're talking about is mine—got that?'

'Sure, Cousin Cormac,' Rodge answered with a broad smile. 'I don't usually filch other men's wives. Lust after them, maybe, but from a distance.'

He put a hand to his ear as if listening for the explosive response, but it seemed that his cousin was not deigning to reply. Rodge followed Lynda into the sitting-room, waiting until Lynda had found a seat, then dropping into a chair.

'Do you want to go on a driveabout?' he asked, his hand covering a yawn. 'Sorry about that—I stayed up into the night with friends.'

Lynda laughed. 'I don't think so, thanks. You might fall asleep at the wheel. Cup of tea?' She stood up.

'I could do with one. Mrs Wendon not here?'

'Cormac told her not to come this weekend.' She went into the kitchen, Rodge following.

'What was the point of that when he's there,' he stabbed the air in the direction of the study, 'and you're here? If he'd intended spending the entire weekend in bed with you, I could have understood it. Come to think of it,' he scratched his head, 'there's a few things I don't understand.'

Lynda stayed silent, making the tea and arranging cups. Then she remembered that she had not asked Cormac if he would like to join them. She told Rodge she wouldn't be a moment, and made for the study.

Cormac looked up swiftly, an odd glitter of anger in his eyes. 'What do you want?'

'I'm making a cup of tea for Rodge and myself.'

'Cosy, aren't you, both of you? It didn't take you long to get on the same wavelength.'

'You haven't even tried to get on to mine,' she pointed out.

'And he has.'

She answered with a reasonably successful attempt to sound offhand, 'He didn't even have to try.' She did not wait for the rejoinder. 'Do you want to join us?'

'Physically, no. But I'd like the tea.'

If his cold look had lingered he would have seen her disconsolate expression.

Rodge commented, as she returned to the kitchen, 'Has he just given you a verbal mauling?'

Lynda lifted a shoulder. 'He's good at it.'

'You know from experience?' Lynda shrugged again. 'Why did you marry Cormac, Lynda?'

'I must take this tea in to him,' she answered, evading the question.

Rodge followed, lingering in the study doorway. Cormac nodded as Lynda placed the cup of tea within his reach. As she left the room, she edged past Rodge, who again followed.

In the sitting-room, she drank her tea, seated in a chair while Rodge occupied one of the settees. 'I said,' he repeated, 'why did you marry my cousin? Will you tell me, or is it so sordid you can't talk about it?'

Lynda laughed at the question. 'Would you believe me if I told you I married him for love?'

'Not after witnessing that little scene, less than twenty-four hours after you married him.'

'Women can wait on the men they love,' she parried.

'And men can be polite to the women they love.' Rodge gulped his tea. 'Maybe you're the sort that likes to be treated as a doormat? Although,' he regarded her reflectively, 'I shouldn't have thought so.'

'You think right.' She smiled, hoping to put him off the scent. 'So I must love him, mustn't I?'

Rodge frowned, brushing back his fair, flopping hair. 'He obviously doesn't appreciate his good luck.'

Lynda said, hoping against hope that Rodge would enlighten her, 'That picture of a woman Cormac has beside his bed——'

'You know about Yolande?'

'No, I don't. Should I, Rodge? You're his cousin. Could you tell me about the part she played in his life?'

Rodge frowned. 'They were going to be married. Didn't you know?'

CHAPTER SIX

LYNDA felt her cheeks drain. She whispered, eyes wide, 'I'm so different from that woman!'

'I told you his taste had improved.'

She could not make a joke of it. The fact was too significant to be treated lightly. If the woman Yolande was Cormac's type of female, then nothing would ever make him change in that respect. It therefore followed, she reasoned agonisingly, that his feelings for herself would never develop into love, nor would he experience anything towards her except a very natural physical desire.

I should have known, she admonished herself yet again. All the same, it was impossibly difficult to accept.

'What went wrong?' she asked. 'He told me he'd been injured going to help a woman—I guess now that it was his fiancée—who'd had an accident while she was skiing, but he collided with another person.'

'You've guessed right,' Rodge told her. 'And that "other person" was another man, the man she abandoned her marriage to Cormac for.'

'I suppose it's beginning to make sense—Cormac's marriage to me, I mean. And to you, surely?'

He watched Lynda's twisting hands. 'Rebound?'

Lynda nodded. 'And to make his ex-fiancée jealous.'

He shook his head. 'She's beyond being made jealous—she's living with the other man.' Lynda said nothing. 'Which brings us back to rebound.' Rodge got up and walked about. 'Cormac said that after Yolande, he'd give any other woman hell.' He stood in front of her. 'The man's a fool. Look at you.' He bent down. 'Eyes that would melt a glacier, a mouth that says "kiss me", a nose that says "keep your distance".' He ran a finger down it. 'Could a man ask for more?'

'You'll get more than you bargained for, Rodge, if you touch my wife again.' Cormac stood in the doorway, the solid frame of him almost filling it.

The eyes of the cousins clashed. 'Dog in the manger, Cormac,' Rodge taunted, 'even if you don't appreciate the lady in question?'

Cormac entered, crutches swinging menacingly. 'Tell me what you came for, Rodge, then get yourself out of my house!'

To Lynda's surprise, Rodge looked a little abashed. 'Okay, Lynda's yours. I wonder if you know how lucky you are?' At the door, he said, 'What I came for can wait—like your honeymoon. Incidentally, Lynda's just told me she married you for love.' He left, hand raised in an ironic salute.

'There was no need,' said Cormac, his voice hard, 'to give credibility to our marriage by pretending you love me. You accepted it, as I did, as a business arrangement. Don't try to colour our relationship with false sentiment.'

'So I should go around telling everyone I hate you?'

'Be honest,' he jeered. 'Be brave and tell them the truth.'

'Do you know,' Lynda rallied, 'it's beginning to be true—the hating part.' Her lip quivered, betraying her vulnerability, and his eyes narrowed, having picked up the signal.

'What you feel for me is of no consequence to me whatsoever.'

Lynda cursed herself for having given herself away. She hurried past him, aghast at his inflexible attitude, wanting to throw herself down and cry her heart out in secret at the foolhardiness of what she had done in agreeing to marry such an implacable man.

His hand shot out and caught her shoulder, pulling her backwards against him. 'I need your help in my work. There are papers to sort through in the study.' He tipped back her head, his fingers soft on her throat. His mouth descended, catching her breath with his kiss. His mouth held hers while his hand moved down to the full swell of her breast, staying there. She felt her own surging reaction to his knowledgeable touch. He lifted his head, mouth smiling, eyes watchful.

Lynda twisted from him, rubbing at her mouth. 'What are you doing,' she defied him, unable to come to terms with his calculated passion, 'giving me that "hell" you vowed you'd give to the next woman in your life?'

'Who told you that little titbit? Rodge? I guessed so.'

'Was it true?' she asked, hoping against hope for a denial. 'Did you say that?'

His cold stare held hers, making her shiver.

'Was that why you were so unpleasant to me last night when we made love?' she persisted, desperate for his answer. 'And why you said just now that you didn't care what I felt for you?'

His jaw moved, but he said nothing.

'All right, so you won't tell me. But tell me something else—why pick on me to wreak your vengeance on?'

His only response was to say tonelessly, 'Come into the study, will you?'

It was next day that Cormac told Lynda about the job he intended giving her at the London office.

It was over coffee that he spoke to her. She had been late down for breakfast, having lain awake for much of the night wondering if he would come to her. He had not put any pressure on her to share his bed, and she had gone to the bed in the smaller room again, partly with relief, partly disappointment.

It wouldn't go, that disappointment, no matter how she tried to rationalise it away. Her mind was disappointed and, she couldn't deny it, her body was disappointed, longing for the touch of Cormac's hands, even for his rough demand.

In the end sleep had come, tiredness dowsing the hope which had kept her pulses beating fast until well into the night.

Cormac held out his cup for more coffee and when she had filled it, he nodded his thanks. He lounged on one of the settees, his bronze-coloured shirt partly unbuttoned, his casual air reflected in his clothes. His tone, however, held a Monday morning briskness, making Lynda despair that any woman, let alone his wife, would ever again be able to find a way through his mental armour.

'You'll have a desk in my office,' he told her. 'You'll be calling up people, talking to contacts all over the world.'

'Sounds like quite a responsible job,' she commented, with a worried frown.

'You'll be able to tackle it,' Cormac assured her. 'I'll nurse you through the early stages.' He smiled. 'It's all part of the package we agreed. Unless, of course, you'd rather stay at home, acting the perfect housewife role all day?'

Lynda shook her head. 'I'd be bored out of my mind.'

'That's what I thought you'd say. There'll be a good salary to go with the job.'

'But you're giving me an allowance.'

'That's in addition. It's what you married me for, wasn't it—money?'

Lynda pulled out of the chair and wandered to the window, staring out. She knew his eyes were on her, she could almost feel them boring into her.

When he spoke again, however, she jumped. 'Would you like to see the cottage your mother's going to live in?'

'Yes, please.' Her voice sounded thin and unhappy.

'Help me, Lynda.' He spoke softly and as she turned immediately, his eyes were smiling along with his mouth. It was as if he had known she would come at his call.

Her hands reached out, but instead of taking them, he pulled her down until she was lying on top of him. 'Your leg!' she exclaimed.

'To hell with it,' he answered, his mouth seeking hers.

Through her dress she felt his thighs pressing into her

soft flesh, and the warm excitement he had aroused in
her before began again. He rolled her until her back
was against the settee's upholstery and shifted so that
they were lying side by side.

There was a growing demand in him that reached out
to her and she felt herself returning his kisses, holding
his shoulders as if she were frightened he would stop.

But stop he did, abruptly, swinging her round and off
him. Lynda scrambled to her feet, shaking a little.
'What's the matter,' she challenged, 'just remembered
my name isn't Yolande? Or is this part of your
campaign to give me hell and reduce me to pleading for
mercy?'

'Neither,' he returned, reaching for his crutches.
'Next time I make love to you, it won't be a skirmish in
the living-room. Nor will it be quickly done and soon
over, like the first time.' He flashed a taunting look. 'I
can't have you running to other men for the satisfaction
your husband refuses to give. So,' he moved his injured
leg to the floor, 'we'll wait.' His hand went out again.

This time, he allowed her to help him to his feet.

'Come,' he said, 'we'll go and look at your mother's
cottage.'

It was a whitewashed, half-timbered little building, the
rear of it approached by a path which wound through a
group of ancient trees. It stood some distance back
from a narrow country lane bordering the rambling and
varied gardens which stretched away from the house.

Cormac unlocked the door and followed Lynda in,
ducking his head to avoid contact with the low lintel.
Since there was no entrance lobby, they had stepped
straight into the living area. There were beams across
the ceiling, and the walls were painted in pleasing pastel
colours. The furniture was comfortable and covered in
green or bronze, with a dining-table under the window
and shaded lamps here and there.

No money had been spared, it seemed, to make the
cottage comfortable. It was even centrally heated,
Lynda was delighted to observe. She wandered into the

small kitchen, saw the modern equipment and revelled in it all, for her mother's sake.

'Oh, she'll love this!' Lynda exclaimed, eyes shining. Making its way upwards was a short flight of stairs. 'May I?' she asked.

'Feel free,' replied Cormac, seeming amused by her appreciation.

The larger bedroom had a small casement window which looked out over a small flower-filled garden bounded by a low white fence. The bed was covered with a flowered quilt, the curtains matched its pattern, as did the cover of the low chair.

Darting into the bathroom, Lynda perceived that it had been created out of a smaller room, but it was as modern as money could make it. Another cubby-hole of a bedroom adjoined the bathroom.

As she descended the stairs, she found Cormac waiting for her.

'Glad you sacrificed yourself to me now you've seen what I'm giving to your mother?' he asked caustically.

Her pleasure was such that she overlooked his sarcasm and answered with sincerity, 'My mother will be so happy here. It's a wonderful little home.'

'Maybe, on reflection,' he eyed her thoughtfully, 'it might have been a better idea not to have married you, but to have given you this place. Then, whenever I felt the need, I could have come over and visited you. How would you have liked my offer if I had proposed the job to you of being not my wife, but my woman?'

'You would never have seen me again,' she answered evenly.

'No?' he jeered. 'With the money I'd have been prepared to give you, you would have done anything. After all, your prime motivation in life is money. You can't deny it, otherwise you wouldn't now be wearing my ring. What other reason, if not money, did you have for marrying me?'

A glance at him showed her again the resolution in his face, the brooding eyes, the curved indentation from nose to chin which drew attention to the firmness of his mouth. She knew the touch of that mouth, delighted in the feel of it against hers, knew the sensation of its ruthless exploration making her want to please and please again.

All this would have to remain a secret for as long as she lived. Even if she ever told him she loved him, he wouldn't believe her. So she lifted her shoulders and answered, 'What other reason?' and closed her eyes so that she would not have to see his contempt.

Cormac had spent the rest of the day working. Lynda wondered whether he had deliberately kept away from her to demonstrate just how little she meant to him.

Despite what he had said about her sleeping with him, it was the smaller room she made for that night. Cormac came to bed much later, but Lynda had not slept. She tried to tell herself that she had not been listening for him, but the moment she heard him enter the larger room, her heart beat faster, and her mind danced with hope.

When the movement of the bed told her he had finally settled down, a wave of hopelessness overcame her, leaving her weary but obstinately sleepless. Growing tired of her own restlessness, she scrambled out, finding her slippers and pulling on her wrap. If she crept across his room quietly enough, she would make it to the door and down to the kitchen for a hot drink. It was, she decided, worth a try. Holding her breath, she turned the handle—the hinges did not creak. She left the door ajar and crept across the room.

Glancing surreptitiously at the large bed, she was frozen by the sight of Cormac lying partially covered, arms upraised to support his head. In the light from the pocket torch she carried, she saw that he was bare from the waist up, and that he was wide awake and watching her!

'Where are you going?' He reached to switch on the shaded bedlight and his powerful shoulders came upright.

'To—to get a drink or something.' She wrenched her

eyes away from him and started to the door. 'I can't sleep, so——'

'Nor can I. I can't imagine the reason,' he responded dryly. 'Come, Lynda, my love,' his voice was deceptively soft, 'let's help each other.'

'No—no, thanks, I——' She almost made it to the door.

'Lynda!' He cracked out her name like a whip. 'Come to me.'

He swung his uninjured leg to the floor, following it more slowly with the other. The cover had become dislodged and she saw that he was naked. Holding on to the bedside table, he stood up, his face registering the faintest hint of pain, but it was immediately banished.

The full strength of his masculinity that hit her eyes as she looked at him drew her towards him like a force so strong she could almost feel it twining itself around her. As she approached, she saw more clearly the scarred leg, the result of the injuries he had sustained when going to another woman's aid—the woman called Yolande, for whose faithlessness she herself was paying the price.

'No, I——' She whisked round to go, but she was too close now to escape his outstretched hand.

He took the torch away and caught her to him, his faint smile misleading since his eyes were coldly estimating. 'We're lovers now, my love,' he said, his fingers pushing through her tousled hair and securing the back of her head. 'There's no need to be shy with me, your husband.'

'I'm not shy!' she threw back, stiffening her neck muscles to resist the pressure of his hand. 'I just can't get to like the thought that I'm second-best to the fiancée who left you for another man.'

'That's too bad,' he said roughly. 'When I proposed this marriage arrangement to you, I told you it would be a normal marriage.'

'But then,' she argued desperately, 'I didn't know you'd been engaged to someone who left you and all

you wanted me for was to work your revenge against
her out of your system, using me as a fall guy——'

His lips cut off her flow of words. While his mouth
impelled her head back, his hand ran the length of her
nightdress-clad body, seeking an entrance to the
warmth of her flesh.

Finding none, it grew impatient and he raised his
head, putting her an arm's distance from him. 'Take off
those things before I tear them,' he ordered.

Lynda began to obey, slipping the wrap from her
shoulders. With her hand on the neckline of her
nightdress, she caught a glimpse of the photograph that
remained on the low table across the bedroom. Her
hand stilled, and her eyes flashed up to his.

'Not in front of that woman,' she declared. 'Second-
best is bad enough, but to have her image looking
on——'

'Get it for me,' he commanded, and watched as she
went to get the photograph. He took it and without a
glance at the subject hurled it across the room. It
landed, by chance, on the sofa on which the woman had
posed, leaving the glass in the frame unbroken.

Impatient now, Cormac slid the straps of the
nightdress from her shoulders. It cascaded to the floor
and she stood naked under his gaze. He had made love
to her on their wedding night, yet she had not then for
one moment felt as vulnerable, nor so emotionally
uncovered as she did now.

Still he held her from him, indulging his eyes before
slaking his sexual thirst. 'You're beautiful, there's no
denying it. I bought myself a bargain when I paid for
you to be my wife!'

She caught her gasp of humiliation with her throat,
but it forced its way through. 'Why you——' Her hand
lifted, but it was caught in a vice of a grip.

His teeth snapped together. 'I'm wasting valuable
time.' He jerked her arm up and used it to compel her
body down to the bed. She tried to swing her legs
round, but he trapped them between his own as he
stood over her.

Fascinated by the sight of his strength and power, Lynda found her will to resist him had drained away. His eyes caressed her supine form and they were alight with a brilliant passion. They lifted at last to search her face and seemed to catch the brightness of her own.

Lynda saw his hands move, felt a frisson of sensation creep over her thighs and shivered as they moved higher, trailing her stomach and finding intimate places, making her muscles clench and her breath come quickly.

'Cormac,' she whispered, straining to touch him.

There was a low laugh and he eased her legs on to the bed, joining her there. His hand stroked her neck, her shoulders, her arms, coming to rest at last on her swelling breasts. His finger flicked both of the hardening tips in turn, then he moved to cover first one and then the other with his mouth.

The action made her desire flare, made her body move in a mad urgency to close the gap between them. Still he held back, moving his lips all over her, leaving a scorching path and making her gasp, 'Please, Cormac, love me!'

Again there was a rumble of laughter. He was on her now and she felt his chest reverberate with it. He was taking his pleasure of her in every way, but she just didn't care any more. She wanted to give to him whatever he wanted, since he was the man she loved and she needed his possession of her to make her life and her happiness complete.

At last he came into her, and her hands stroked him feverishly, feeling the rippling movement of muscle, the moisture on his skin. Now his fervent possession was lifting her, making her mindless and weightless, and she was pulsating with him, until there was a summit achieved and conquered and joy broke through like sunshine, flooding her being.

They lay entwined and she listened to his breathing, thinking he was asleep. Her mouth touched his cheek and he stirred, and she wanted to tell him, 'I love you,' but the words could not be allowed to break through.

He would, if she said them, make a cynical remark, and that would shatter the cocoon of delight in which she was wrapped.

'Sleep now, my love,' he said softly, and for a sublime moment it seemed as if he almost meant the endearment he had spoken. 'Cover us,' he muttered, and she found the quilt and pulled it across them. 'Come into me,' he said, and she did, pressing the length of her body against him. His arms enfolded her and together they slept.

When morning came, Lynda was both lethargic and excited. It was a curious mixture that had her opening her eyes and wondering about the cause. Then she remembered and reached out to find Cormac. Only the dent in his pillow was left.

There was the sound of water rushing in the adjoining bathroom. Of course, she thought, the weekend was gone and now it was Monday. Their honeymoon, all two days of it, was over.

Pushing back the cover, Lynda saw that she was still naked and that her nightclothes lay where they had been dropped. Scrambling from the bed, she bent down to retrieve them, rising quickly only to discover that Cormac stood in the doorway to the bathroom, a towel around his waist, watching her with a reminiscent smile.

Lynda lifted her clothes in front of her, hearing him say, 'So you aren't shy, or so you said last night?' He approached, to her surprise using only one crutch. Tilting her chin, he brushed his lips from one side of her mouth to the other. 'We may not make love in the true sense of the word, you and I, but we make good memories together. Hm?'

She wanted to say, I have the love, you only have the need, but she stayed silent and nodded. Her nightclothes were bunched into a ball, giving her no cover, and his glance slid over the smooth paleness of her body, bringing colour to it even as he looked.

He laughed and for the moment that his customary harshness was banished, his face was transformed, sending her heart spinning.' He took away the soft bundle, throwing it on to the bed, then bent and kissed the hardening points of her breasts. He was rekindling her desire and he knew it, it couldn't be more evident beneath his lips. He ran a possessive hand over her waist and hips.

'I'd bed you now,' he muttered, 'if a day's work wasn't waiting for me.' He half turned, then swung back. 'And for you, Mrs Daly.' The smile he tossed over his shoulder was genuine and Lynda felt a lightning-strike of pleasure at the way he spoke her new name.

She nodded, running to the smaller room for her clothes. She met him a few moments later at the bathroom door. 'Do I have time to take a shower?'

'As the chairman's wife, you have as much time as you like.'

Lynda shook her head. 'That can't really be true, because I'm in your employment.'

Dark eyebrows arched and he tied the belt of his robe. 'You require payment for the pleasure you gave me last night?'

She coloured deeply, shaking her head. 'You know that's not what I meant.'

'Do I?' His grey eyes had hardened and Lynda suppressed a shiver.

'I'm going to work for you, you said. As your personal assistant.'

'Ah, yes.' Cormac's eyelids drooped momentarily. 'I shall work you until you drop.'

'That's right,' she came back sarcastically, 'get your money's worth!'

His smile this time paid only lip-service to sincerity. He moved on, still using only one crutch.

'Cormac?'

'Yes?' He pulled on a shirt.

'You seem to be putting more weight on your injured leg. Is it getting better?'

'Slowly. Why?' His back was still to her. 'Do you see the end of our marriage in sight already, because my need of your—services will end sooner than you anticipated?'

The colour began to leave her cheeks. 'I didn't even think about that. It wasn't in my mind at all.'

'Nor was it in mine.' He turned towards her, fastening the buttons at his neck. 'According to you, I need you in order to work off my feelings of revenge against my ex-fiancée. In which case,' he seized the crutch and approached slowly, 'injured leg or no injured leg, my need of you will continue until that craving for revenge has been exhausted. Which, my love,' he lifted her chin, and held her eyes with the steely grey of his, 'with all the physical attractions you have to offer me, may well take a very long time.'

Mrs Wendon saw them off to work. Her husband, Jack, drove the car into London.

Cormac lounged darkly against the luxurious red upholstery. Lynda wished she could stretch out her hand and find his, as any woman in love with a man who loved her might do. When she thought about his absence of feeling towards her, she experienced a terrible sense of emptiness.

Their intimate encounter last night had been like a sudden and momentary flowering of the desert. He had been right when he had declared, before their marruage, that although it would be devoid of love, it would not be lacking in warmth. With that thought she had to content herself.

He returned to using the two crutches after Lynda had helped him out of the car. After giving instructions to Jack Wendon about the time to return that evening, Cormac turned to Lynda.

'I see you're wondering why I'm taking the weight off my leg again.' He made for the steps up to the glass entrance doors. 'The pain returned after breakfast.' He flashed her a meaningful look. 'The anaesthetic effect of our night of lovemaking must have worn off!'

He brought the colour to her cheeks as he had plainly meant to. Mick, the doorman, had seen Cormac approaching, and he swung the door wide, giving a faintly ingratiating bow.

' 'Morning, Mr Daly. Oh, and Mrs Daly. You look lovely, Mrs Daly,' he added. 'I heard the wedding went off very well.'

Lynda smiled and nodded, but could not forget the morning he had checked up on her when she had returned to the office building for that abortive photographic session with Larry Chapman. Then she reminded herself that Mick had been acting on instructions—from the man at her side who was now her husband.

At her side he might be, she thought, walking with him out of the lift, but he had in the hour or so since they had left the house grown as remote from her as he ever had been before their brief engagement.

Betty Peters reached out her hand to Lynda as they entered. 'You look wonderful, Mrs Daly,' she said with evident pleasure. 'Life has some very strange tricks and surprises up its sleeve, hasn't it?'

Lynda knew she was referring to events of the recent past, to the address which she herself had been instructed to pass to her, plus her own insistence that she should try that place for a job. She nodded, smiling, but felt just a twist of embarrassment that Cormac's secretary knew so much.

'Who knew that such a meeting in my house,' Cormac remarked, moving towards his room, 'would be the curtain-raiser to our falling in love?'

Lynda experienced a rush of gratitude at Cormac's attempt to put matters into perspective in his secretary's eyes. Or was it, after all, an attempt to protect himself from criticism for his apparently capricious action in marrying a girl so low down in the hierarchical scale?

Whatever his motive, Lynda had to acknowledge that it made her feel just a bit easier in her relations with at least one member of his staff.

Cormac explained to Mrs Peters that he wanted another desk brought into his office for his wife's use. 'She will be lightening the load for me,' he stated, 'and I hope, for you. Also, whenever I need physical help, she'll be here and I won't have to trouble you.'

'It was no trouble, Mr Daly,' his secretary said dutifully, but from Cormac's sideways glance, Lynda knew the situation had brought its own difficulties where Betty Peters was concerned.

Lynda removed the jacket of the dark blue outfit she wore, revealing the blue-grey blouse with its short sleeves and softly feminine frilled neckline. She noticed that Cormac, still standing, was removing his own jacket, and went to help him. He seemed about to object but appeared to change his mind, accepting her assistance.

With her help again, he found his seat, and Lynda was sure he was suppressing a shaft of pain from his leg. 'Do you have to attend the doctor,' she ventured, 'for treatment or anything?'

'Yes, yes,' he answered irritably. He turned flinty-grey eyes up to her. 'And I don't need your pity.'

Lynda compressed her lips, silencing her defensive retort. The phone rang and Cormac answered. It was a call he seemed to be expecting. She went to stare through the window, watching the unceasing traffic as it passed both ways along the wide sweep of the Strand. Across the road were a variety of shops, but the passers-by stopped to look in their windows only occasionally. It was getting-to-work time, and too early probably for tourists to be about.

Lynda tuned in to Cormac's conversation—it seemed to be an overseas call. As he put down the receiver, Betty Peters knocked and entered. 'The desk has arrived, Mr Daly, plus a chair. Where do you want the men to put them?'

Cormac indicated a corner across the large room. The office furniture was carried in, placed in position, and the two men departed.

'Lynda, take one of my telephones. There's a socket for it somewhere near your desk. Here,' he tapped a green instrument, 'this one. Betty,' to Mrs Peters, 'she'll require a typewriter, plus the usual additions.'

'I'll see what I can do, Mr Daly.' The secretary hurried away, only to be called back by her employer.

'The small office next to mine, is it still unoccupied?' Betty nodded. 'I want that furnished, too. My wife can use that when I have clients here so that we can, if necessary, talk privately.' Betty Peters nodded and went on her way.

That, Lynda reflected, adjusting the height of her chair, puts me in my place and no doubt about it! If she hadn't had the memory of Cormac's lovemaking still imprinted on her mind and, here and there, her body, she would, she reflected, have been convinced she was once again a mere employee of Daly Enterprises.

Cormac had given her a pile of papers to read. This she did with some eagerness. She would show Cormac that she could tackle the work, she would make him acknowledge her potential!

Partway through the morning, after taking a succession of phone calls, Cormac ran a hand through his hair. Lynda watched him covertly, wishing she could run to him and hold him until he relaxed in her arms.

His eyes roamed round the room, settling for a second on her, then passing on.

'Lynda.' She met his eyes. 'Get me a drink. That cabinet—you'll find a few bottles in there. I want the usual—Scotch.'

'Cormac? At this time of the day?'

'For God's sake, don't lecture me like a nervous wife! Let me assure you that I harbour no inclinations whatsoever towards alcoholism. I have a leg that sometimes drives me mad, and this is one of those times. Unless,' his eyes printed out a male message as she rose with obvious reluctance, 'you'd like to provide me with the anaesthetic you gave me so freely in the night?'

Forcing herself not to react to his taunt, Lynda gave him the drink he required, closing the doors on the various bottles which, she knew, were there for the entertainment of privileged visitors.

He took a drink. 'Have one youself,' he invited on

a note of mockery, then tossed the rest down his throat.

She shook her head, saying nothing, and the glass banged down. 'Stop looking so pious! We all have our weaknesses, and one of mine is trying to mask the pain I get. The other, as you know, is the need of a woman in my bed.'

Again, Lynda schooled herself to show no angry response, hiding the hurt he seemed to delight in inflicting. 'When you've stopped reducing me to size,' she said with a false calm, 'I'll continue with my reading.'

'Will you, indeed?' The drink seemed to have uncoiled a spring inside him. He pressed a button and spoke into the intercom on his desk. 'Deflect all calls,' he told his secretary. 'I'm out to everyone until further notice.'

'Yes, Mr Daly,' Betty Peters answered.

'Now,' Cormac flashed a look at Lynda, 'come over here, please.' Automatically, she obeyed. 'Pull up a chair. You and I are going to spend some time together in conference on the function and duties of a personal,' his glance dropped to the swell of her breasts beneath the sheen of her blouse, 'very personal, assistant.'

Lynda waited, wishing his nearness did not fill her mind to the extent of pushing away all other thoughts. If only she could force herself to concentrate, she knew she would soon learn anything he might attempt to teach her.

'Get me those folders over there, will you?' Cormac directed briskly. As she went to the long table on which the folders lay, she told herself that her employer-husband would allow nothing—neither her proximity and certainly no emotion—to mist over his brain nor unbalance his judgment.

So why should I? she asked herself, knowing the answer even before she had finished asking herself the question. Dominant in her mind was her love for him, whereas for her, he had nothing but his very male reflexes.

'Take this account,' he was saying, 'Kitchenware——'
He turned a smile on to her that melted her bones.
'That should ring a bell!'

Lynda could not stop herself from smiling back. She
shook her head. 'It tolls a bell. There's a difference.'

He laughed and her heartbeats broke the speed limit.
'The end of the road for you with this company—or so
you thought at the time.'

'So did you,' she retorted.

His eyebrows lifted. 'Did I?' He had slipped back into
his boss personality. 'Kitchenware by Brightling. It
wants to break into new overseas markets. Okay?'
Lynda nodded, holding herself rigid, trying not to be
conscious of his broad shoulders abutting hers, the faint
fragrance of his shaving lotion, the sweep of his jaw.

'Are you with me?' She jumped as he jerked her
attention back, and she nodded frantically. Cormac's
eyes slipped down her arms to her clenched hands.
'Relax, pet,' he said softly, separating her hands with
his. He ran his thumb over her moistened palms.
'Nervous? Of me, your lover?' He was baiting her and
she jerked free of his touch.

'Shall we continue?' she asked, as coolly as she could
manage.

He gave her a sarcastic look. 'Why not?' was his
equally cool reply. He returned his attention to the
folder in question. 'Travelling overseas is expensive, so
before we buy ourselves an air ticket, we use the phone.
Right?'

'Right. So we do our "homework" first, by calling up
contacts in the countries concerned?'

'Full marks,' he said with a wide smile, drawing a
smile from her. His gaze lingered on her lips and he
seemed to have difficulty drawing it away. 'We saturate
ourselves with information, with background material.
In other words, we research our markets fully before we
ever set foot on a plane.'

It was lunchtime before he called his secretary to tell
her he was free again. He told Lynda, 'I'm lunching
with a client.'

Momentarily disconcerted, she asked, 'So where do I eat?'

'Wherever you like, for as long as you like.'

'That's not right,' she addressed him from her desk. 'I work for the company as an employee, not a director, so I work an employee's hours.'

Cormac answered distantly, 'It's for me to decide the hours you work.'

Her shoulders lifted. 'If you want my working day to be elastic to fit in with yours, I can't stop you, but I'm taking the usual hour for lunch.'

'As you like,' he returned coldly, collecting together the papers they had been reading.

Pulling on her jacket, she said, 'Cormac?' He looked up, his face blank. 'I think——' she moistened her lips '—I think it would be more—well, professional if I called myself Lynda Groome during working hours.'

He snapped his briefcase shut. 'As you wish.' Reaching for his crutches, he said, 'Help me, will you?' It was an order, not a question.

When she touched him, she hoped he would not feel the faint tremble of her hands. The longing to fling her arms around his neck was so great she could hardly control them.

At the door, she asked, 'What shall I do if I'm back from lunch before you?'

'Just carry right on reading,' answered Cormac, making for his secretary's office.

Lynda made her way along the corridor to the lift. She had decided to eat in the staff dining-room as she had in the old days. It was possible that she might meet Mandy there.

Coming out of the lift was a tall young man with fair hair and surprise in his eyes. 'What the heck are you doing here?' asked Rodge Miller, as the lift doors closed behind him.

Lynda watched it go without her. 'I might ask you that. How long have you been working for Daly

Enterprises?' She had meant it as a joke, thinking Rodge had called in to see Cormac.

Rodge consulted his watch. 'Approximately four hours.'

'Today's your first day? What's your job?'

'Studio manager. Took the place of one Larry Chapman.'

Lynda frowned. 'Larry's gone? Since when, Rodge?'

'Ask the boss.' He grinned. 'You know him well enough by now. Look,' he glanced at his watch, 'I've got a lunch date. Ex-girl-friend—well, almost ex. We were going to have a heart-to-heart, but even that isn't really necessary.'

Lynda smiled up at him. 'Parting with understanding on both sides?' Rodge nodded. 'So it's a goodbye meal.'

'By this afternoon, I'll be free to let my eyes roam again.'

'I bet you won't be womanless for long,' she commented.

He grinned, shaking his head. 'I won't be in a hurry to tie myself up. This one hurt somewhat. Men do get hurt, you know that?' He lifted his hand, started to go, then stopped. 'You haven't told me what you're doing here.'

'Save it for next time, Rodge. Enjoy your lunch.'

He made a face and hurried away.

Lynda went into the staff dining-room. She saw the moving crowd, heard the noise and inhaled the familiar food smell. For a few seconds, the whole scene seemed to stand on its head and she felt as out of place as a kitten in a tiger's cage.

What had happened to her? Little over a month ago, she had walked daily into this place as if she had been part of the wallpaper. Now, she felt an overpowering shyness and an urge to walk away. This she would have done had a voice to one side of her not said.

'Lynda? You look great. Where've you been? Haven't seen you for days.'

'Liz, it's nice to see you.' Lynda listened to herself greeting the girl who used to occupy a desk not far from her own. Even my voice sounds strained, she thought. Why don't I fit in any more? Liz was lingering, seeming to want an explanation. 'I'm married,' Lynda told her, clasping her hands together so that Liz wouldn't see the extravagance of her engagement ring.

'Isn't that just great!' Liz exclaimed. 'It suits you.' The girl gave her a sly look. 'Is he tall, dark and——'

'Handsome, yes. It was a bit sudden, but we . . .' What can I tell her? Lynda wondered. 'We couldn't wait.' She broadened her smile until it hurt, then diverted Liz's attention by saying, 'I'm looking for Mandy. Know where she is?'

'She's right over there—look at her waving. Well, great to have seen you,' added Liz, going on her way.

Lynda pushed through the crowd to join Mandy at her table. There were two others, young men who were absorbed in their conversation to the exclusion of everyone else, and for this, Lynda was glad.

Mandy was half standing, reaching out and grabbing Lynda's shoulder. 'You look wonderful! Take a seat. Can't believe it was only three days ago. What are you eating?'

Lynda was laughing, peeling off her jacket, pulling up her chair. 'I haven't had time to get myself some food. I was looking for you and saw Liz Brown, but I'll get myself a tray.' She started up, but Mandy's hand was waving, telling her to stay where she was.

'Salad, like you used to have? Okay, I'll get it. Anything else? Coffee?'

'Mandy, I'll——'

'No, you won't. Can't have the chairman's wife getting her own meal. It's enough that you've come here.'

'Look, Mandy, don't let it make any difference,' implored Lynda. 'Try to forget it, will you?'

Mandy pulled a face. 'I can't really forget, can I? Hang on while I get you something to eat.' She was gone ten minutes but returned triumphant.

'People have noticed you, but they don't even realise you disappeared from the place. Here's your meal.' She

told Lynda the cost and accepted the money, pushing it
into her purse. 'Tell me,' curiosity was scrawled across
her elfin face, 'how's life—you know what I mean—
treating you?'

'It's okay, Mandy.' At her friend's disappointed
frown, Lynda added, 'You want a happy-ever-after
version? It's more than okay. It's just great, Mandy.'
She heard her own voice trail off. 'I mean that.'

'You do love him, don't you?' Mandy sounded
worried.

'Very much. More now than ever. But——' Lynda
started on her salad.

'Somehow I knew there'd be a "but"!' Mandy looked
right and left. 'You can't tell me now, can you? Not
here, with all this crowd. When will you be this way
again?'

'At the office? Every day—I'm working for the
company. It's a complicated story.'

Lynda ate in silence for some minutes while Mandy
stirred her coffee, frowning at it. When Lynda had
finished and was on to her own coffee, she said, 'Want
to hear some news? Or maybe you know it already.
Remember Rodge Miller, Cormac's cousin?'

Mandy's eyes brightened. 'Do I not! Don't tell me,
he's a devoted family man.'

'After lunchtime today, he'll be free to roam again—
or so he said just now when I saw him,' Lynda told her.
'He said he was just breaking up with current girl-
friend.'

Mandy finished her coffee and opened her eyes wide.
'You saw him—just now? Where, in the street?'

'Right here in this building. It was his first day today
working for Daly Enterprises.'

'You didn't mean it?'

Lynda nodded. 'He's taken Larry Chapman's place
as studio manager. Did you know Larry had left?'

'I did know,' Mandy answered slowly. 'What I didn't
know was who had taken over his job.'

'What happened with Larry, Mandy? Did he leave
voluntarily or was he fired?'

'He's got another job. Rumour says it was both ways—he left because he'd found somewhere else, and he was given the push. You choose, like I did.'

'You don't mean Cormac threw him out?'

'Don't sound so horrified, Lynda. After what he did to that girl Amy from Sales and then to you.' Her face changed as she remembered. 'So Rodge Miller has Larry's job.'

'You might even meet him around the place,' Lynda teased.

'He wouldn't recognise me. What impression would someone like me make on the cousin of the chairman?'

'He took your phone number.'

'And probably tore it up the minute he got home.' She shook her head. 'It was nice while it lasted—all of an hour.'

Lynda laughed with her, then said she must go. 'I'll tell you about my job some time,' she promised as they parted.

Cormac was missing when Lynda returned to his office. Betty Peters came in, having heard the door open. 'These business lunches of Mr Daly's,' she explained, 'they can go on for hours. But it's surprising how much those working meals achieve sometimes.'

This was an aspect of Cormac's work that was unknown to her. There was, she thought, so much about him she didn't know. Removing her jacket, she smiled at Betty Peters. 'Thanks for telling me.'

Betty came farther into the room. 'I'm so glad you're here, Mrs Daly, to look after Mr Daly. Although I didn't really mind helping Mr Daly, it was awkward sometimes being interrupted so much in my work. And his moods have been black since his accident.'

'Before that,' Lynda probed, 'was he easier to work for?'

'Well,' she smiled with a touch of embarrassment, 'he's very precise and I've usually managed to please him. I suppose he wouldn't have kept me on if I hadn't.'

'Well,' Lynda remarked, taking her seat, 'I can lift a load from your shoulders now I'm here, can't I?'

The phone rang in Betty's office and she dashed to answer it. Alone again, Lynda wondered how soon her own shoulders would begin to sag with the weight of responsibility she seemed to have taken on. She had encountered Cormac's moodiness, but she suspected he could prove to be even more difficult than he had so far revealed himself to be.

Well, she thought, I have one weapon I can use to soothe him . . . Then her mind caught up with her emotions and she blushed at the image that had splashed itself across her brain—of Cormac's tall, strong body, of her own wild desire springing to life under his kissess and caresses.

Pulling the folders towards her, she hastily rearranged her thoughts. Even the idea of him aroused in her an unbearable longing, so how could she ever hope to concentrate on her work when he was actually there in person?

For a time, she read the papers he had given her, then a call came through from Mrs Peters. 'There's a firm on the phone called Home-aid Planners, Mrs Daly—said they wanted to speak to Mr Daly. Normally, I would say he was out, but I wondered if you'd like to have a go at dealing with them? They sound quite eager, and they'd be a new customer.'

Lynda wrote down the name. 'Anyone special calling? I see, a Mr Colling. Well, I'll see what I can do, Mrs Peters, but I hope I don't frighten them off!'

The secretary laughed. 'I'll put them through. And please call me Betty. Your husband does.'

'Mr Colling?' said Lynda in her most confident voice. 'I'm Mr Daly's personal assistant. My name is Lynda——' for a fraction of a moment she hesitated '—Lynda Groome.'

The voice that replied was brisk. 'I'll put you in the picture, Miss Groome. We're a growing company catering for the needs of the home—not from the purely domestic angle, you understand, but in providing aids for easier living.'

'I see,' Lynda replied encouragingly, thinking thankfully, so far, so good.

'We have just taken under our wing a small company manufacturing a new product—a small domestic dust extractor, intended for installation in every room in the house.'

'Very labour-saving,' Lynda commented with enthusiasm. 'Excellent idea.'

'Glad you like the sound of it, Miss Groome,' the caller replied. 'We want to establish a market for this piece of equipment not only in this country, but eventually, a number of the developed countries overseas.'

'And you'd like us to handle this aspect of your marketing?' she asked.

'Both aspects, Miss Groome. You're an established firm with, I might add, a high reputation for getting results, which is why we're placing our confidence in you.'

'Thank you, Mr Colling,' Lynda answered. 'I'll pass your comments and requirements on to Mr Daly and I'm sure he'll be in touch.'

The caller thanked her, saying he was obliged for her polite and sympathetic attention and rang off. Lynda sighed with relief at her own achievement, then remembered she had forgotten to ask the company's address. Hand to head, she ran to Betty Peters' office.

'It's all right, Mrs Daly,' said Betty, 'I took a note of it from Mr Colling's secretary. Did you cope?'

'Well, he thanked me for my politeness and seemed quite pleased, but all I did was make sympathetic noises.'

'At that early stage,' Betty explained, 'that's really all that's required. Your husband will be pleased, won't he, when you tell him.'

I doubt it, Lynda thought, but did not say so. It's what he's paying me for, after all. But she smiled and nodded and returned to the other room.

A few minutes later, the phone on her desk rang

again. This time there was no intermediary in the form
of Betty. 'Lynda?' Cormac asked, 'I won't be back this
afternoon. Make your own way home. I'll see you this
evening.'

'Yes, Mr——' Her hand flew to her mouth.

'For God's sake, I'm your husband!'

Why did he sound so angry? she wondered. 'Yes,
Cormac,' she answered with assumed meekness, at
which he hammered the receiver home.

Home, she thought, fighting the disappointment she
felt at his continuing absence—when will I start looking
on Cormac's house as my home? Yet she felt no desire
to return to the conditions in which she had so recently
lived. She wouldn't have fitted in there now any more
than she felt she had in the staff restaurant.

Had she changed so fundamentally in just a few
days? Looking back, she realised that in the two weeks
or so that had passed since Cormac's proposal of
marriage, she had been gearing herself up mentally for
the total alteration in her life style. By the time she was
actually required to live Cormac's way and in his
surroundings, she had been ready for the changeover.

She had, in fact, tutored herself into the dual role
expected of her—that of wife to the company chairman,
and also that of his personal assistant. Which, she
realised, was why she had been able to deal without too
much difficulty with that phone call from the new
clients.

Later, walking along the drive to Whitegates, she
stared at the house. She pictured Cormac seated in the
living-room, waiting impatiently for her return. The day
had drained her, but she told herself it had been her
first day in a new job. Nor could she overlook the fact
that working in the same room as Cormac, feeling so
near to him, yet so far away because of his indifference
to her, had taken its toll of her emotionally.

He was not where she had imagined him to be. Mrs
Wendon greeted her, saying that her husband Jack was
bringing Mr Daly home and wasn't it a pity they
couldn't have picked up Mrs Daly, too?

Lynda climbed the stairs to the bedroom, wandering to the window. Her eyes sought out the place in the spacious gardens where her mother's cottage stood. An unexpected wish to see her mother again, to talk to her and pour out her heart overwhelmed her. Wasn't there anyone she could tell about her love for her husband and how it hurt that he didn't return that love?

CHAPTER SEVEN

A SHOWER refreshed her, and as she dried herself, she felt her skin glow, and the blood race around her veins. The extension telephone rang and she grabbed the blue robe from the door, smiling as the sleeves hung over her hands and the hem almost touched her ankles.

Was it Cormac again, telling her he wouldn't return before nightfall?

'Lynda?' It was her mother's voice, full of affection. 'I've been thinking of you a lot. How are you, dear? And Cormac?'

Staring out of the window over the green lawns and wide-branched trees, Lynda answered, 'Everything's fine. Life's good, Mum,' it came pouring out of her, 'marriage is wonderful! I'm happy, truly I am.'

All she had said was true, yet there was the one vital element missing—and of this she could say nothing to her mother.

'That's wonderful to hear, Lynda. So it was all true when you told me you loved him.'

'It was true then, Mum,' she reassured her mother, 'and it's true now. I love Cormac, if anything, even more. Do you know,' she went on, sitting on a corner of the small table and still facing the window, 'I can almost see where your cottage is from here?'

'So we won't be that far apart, will we?' Rose responded. 'I'm moving in tomorrow. Did you know?'

Lynda frowned. 'Cormac didn't tell me.' Why hadn't he? she wondered. 'That's great news. I must tell you, Mum—this afternoon, while Cormac was out, I got us a new customer. I talked to the representative and he seemed to like what I said, so I've achieved something positive even on my first day.'

'I'm glad for you, Lynda. Was Cormac pleased?'

'He doesn't know yet. When he comes home I'll——'

A noise behind her made her jump and swivel round. Cormac was leaning against the door. Had he been there long? 'He's here, Mum. I'll see you tomorrow evening. Good luck with the move. 'Bye for now.'

Lynda stood up and the long sleeves covered her hands. She made a hurried move towards the smaller room and tripped over the robe's hem. In spite of his injury, Cormac must have moved with the speed of a panther, catching her with his free arm while the other supported him with the aid of a crutch.

Flushed, confused and feeling like a child caught rifling the biscuit tin, she straightened up and faced him. 'I was taking a shower when my mother rang, so I took your robe . . .'

'I can think of something better to wrap around you after a shower than my robe.' He eased away the arms that were holding it closed. It fell open and Lynda had the mad urge to cover herself. He must have felt the instinctive movement, since his hold on her wrists tightened, keeping her arms spread wide while he looked his fill at the full, tautening shapeliness of her.

'Let me get dressed, Cormac,' she pleaded, but found herself against him, wrapped in his arms, her head back and receiving his probing kisses, going limp under their gasping impact.

He still wore his jacket and she felt the abrasion of his clothes kindling her skin until it burned with the need to feel his skin against hers. He held her away, eyes hard with his driving male need.

'I'm taking a shower,' he said, 'then——'

The phone rang and he cursed. Lynda pulled free and ran to answer it. After a moment, she said, 'Mrs Wendon says dinner will be ready in five minutes.'

'Tell her to hold it back.' He removed his jacket.

Defying him, Lynda told the caller, 'We'll be down very soon, Mrs Wendon.' She hung up and made for the smaller room, evading Cormac's outstretched claw of a hand and laughing at him.

'You little——' He snapped off the word, eyes slitted.

Hurriedly, her body still heated from her brief

encounter with him, she slipped off the towelling robe and found fresh underwear. Turning, she saw that he was watching her. His hand came out, indicating the robe. She picked it up and handed it to him, feeling every movement of his eyes as if they were touching her.

'Please go,' she whispered, but he stayed where he was, by the door.

'Carry on.' It was an order she had no choice but to obey.

Through every personal item she put on, his deliberate appraisal did not waver. At last, she tugged her dress over her head and pulled up the front zip-fastener, the length of which was hidden behind a pleated frill.

Turning her back to inspect her appearance in the mirror, she saw how well the fitted, coral-pink dress suited her, and how the frill, continuing around the collar, framed her face. The colour contrasted well with her dark brown hair, emphasising also the blueness of her eyes.

Facing him again, she snapped, 'Have you seen enough?'

'Too much,' was his mocking retort. 'I'd have preferred you as you were, or in the outfit you wore for that abortive series of shots which the former studio manager took of you on the inflatable poolside bed.'

'Do I deduce from that statement,' she challenged, 'that you sacked Larry Chapman and that he didn't resign willingly from his job?'

'Deduce what the hell you like,' he answered, turning away and limping across to the bathroom, the robe over his arm.

Over dinner, he questioned her about the new client he had overheard her telling her mother she had acquired for the company. She explained the situation, and he appeared interested.

'So,' he said later as she helped him lower himself to one of the settees, 'you think I should be pleased with you.'

'Yes, I think you should,' she answered with a smile.

'I'm a novice at the game, and on my first day, too.'
Cormac pulled her down beside him and she found
herself nearer to him than she had anticipated. His
thigh was so close she wanted to rest her hand on it, but
she dragged her eyes away, only to feel her hand being
moved from her lap.

Her head swung back and she saw that he had placed
it, palm down, exactly where her glance had lingered.

'I am pleased with you,' he declared huskily. Then his
glance grew mocking. 'Especially when I hear you say,
with such fierce insistence, that you love me.' His hand
moved hers backwards and forwards along his thigh as
he watched her through narrowed eyes.

It was his injured leg, but above the injury, and
Lynda felt the hardness of muscle beneath her palm,
telling her a tale of agility and exercise; of his life before
the accident, of athleticism tempering the times when,
as a result of his work, he was trapped by his desk.

He removed his hand and hers went on its way,
backwards and forwards, while her pulses leapt like
hurdlers over fences, racing compulsively on. Wasn't
this what she had longed to do all day—touch him, feel
his iron-hardness beneath her venturing hand?

There was a tap at the door and Mrs Wendon carried
in the coffee tray. Lynda made to lift her hand, but his
came down, securing it. Mrs Wendon smiled serenely at
the incontrovertible evidence of love and left them with
dreamy eyes.

Lynda pulled her hand free. 'I had to tell my mother
I loved you. If I hadn't, she would have started
worrying and doubting whether she should move into
the cottage tomorrow.' She poured the coffee, handing
Cormac a cup. 'Why didn't you tell me you'd made
arrangements for her to move? Maybe you meant it to
be a surprise?' Her smile was winning, but it won no
answering smile from him.

His lifted shoulders dismissed the possibility. 'It was
part of the financial package agreed between us,
remember?'

The statement diluted her potent pleasure at the

increasing intimacy between them. She should have known, she thought, that only a man in love contrived to give his wife or his woman a pleasing surprise.

'Will you contact that firm who called today—Home-aid Planners?'

'Is that their name?' He smiled. 'Don't worry, I won't let your pet project elude your little grasping hand. On behalf of the company, of course.' He took her hand and turned it palm upwards, curling his fingers inward.

Lynda stiffened. 'Is that how you see me, as grasping? Why don't you understand that I'm not motivated by money?'

He released her hand. 'So why did you marry me?'

The question silenced her. How could she tell him the true reason? Even if she did, he would only laugh and tell her to drop the pretence. To fill the silence, she collected the coffee cups on to the tray.

'I saw the doctor this afternoon,' he told her casually.

Her head shot round. 'Is there something wrong?'

He laughed at her concern. 'Doing your damnedest, aren't you, to behave like a loving, tender-hearted wife.' His head rested back. 'It was a routine visit.'

'Betty Peters told me it was a prolonged working lunch.'

He smiled. 'I had told her not to divulge my whereabouts to anyone. She obviously took that 'anyone' to include my wife. However,' his hand reached for hers again, 'I did have a meal with a client, then I continued on to my appointment with the doctor.'

Lynda liked the feel of his feathering fingers over her palm too much to pull her hand away. 'How is your leg coming on?' she asked.

'There's been a marked improvement. The surgeon suggested that my next operation might be brought forward.'

'You have to have another operation?'

Again, Cormac smiled at her worried expression. 'Naturally. They have to remove the bits and pieces they put into my leg to help the fracture to heal.'

'After that, how long will it be before your leg is back to normal?'

His hand was moving on her arm, up and down, bringing to it a life all its own. 'How long does Nature take to do her work? Your guess is as good as mine, or the doctor's.' He pulled her down, so that she had to lift her legs to the settee. His chest was beneath her cheek, the beat of his heart filling her ears. His uninjured leg joined his other reclining one and his arms, as they lifted her the length of him, were evidence of his sleeping strength. 'Indulging in a countdown to the start of our divorce proceedings?'

Lynda shook her head, feeling the roughness of his cheek with its faint evening-time stubble. She couldn't tell him that dread had indeed filled her mind at his disclosure of his fast-approaching return to normality.

His hands cupped her face, holding her away while his serious grey eyes searched out her features, one by one. Then he pulled her head down, pushing his mouth against hers until her lips opened to him.

She gripped his shoulders, feeling through his shirt the dark chest hairs, and still the kiss held. His hand pushed between them, undoing his shirt buttons. It found the zip fastener at the front of her dress and slid it down, and then unhooked the front opening of her bra.

A moment later her breasts felt the rough softness of his chest hairs and the hard wall of flesh beneath them. The intimacy he had brought about produced a throb in her veins. When he held her breast in his palm, circling the sensitive tip with his thumb, she reached up feverishly with her mouth to re-establish the kiss. He put her to one side and took the kiss over until she felt her mouth was no longer hers but his to do with as he wished.

When he ended the kissing and lifted his head, his eyes were bright with male need. 'I'd take you now,' he said, 'if there weren't any danger of interruption.'

Lynda could only gaze at him, her mouth still feeling the driving pressure of his, yet still strangely needing a renewal of his probing possessiveness.

His finger ran down her cheek, then diverted across the moist fullness of her lips. 'There's warmth in our marriage, just as I told you, even though there's no love between us.'

But there is, she wanted to cry, I love you more than I ever thought it possible to love a man. She smiled and lifted her hand to run its back around his roughening chin. He responded by stroking the back of his hand over her thrusting, enticing breasts.

'Cormac,' she whispered, resting her cheek against his neck, 'oh, Cormac, I wish——' I wish you loved me, she was going to say, but what would have been the use? Might as well wish like a child to be able to take the moon out of the sky . . .

'You wish?' he said against her ear, each movement of his lips a kiss.

She shivered as his tongue ran around her ear's curves. 'It doesn't matter.'

'Tell me, my love. If it's anything money can buy, you'll have it, I promise.'

It took a few seconds for the message in Cormac's words to register on Lynda's mind. She shook her head free of his mouth and stared into his face. The full lines of his lips were so near she had only to pout hers to touch them. She saw the faint shading of his upper lip and, higher, the fleeting coolness of his eyes.

No matter what I do, she despaired, nothing seems to alter his opinion of me as a grasping, acquisitive woman. She jerked herself upright and he let her go, as if sensing he had angered her. His distant smile told her that if he had, he did not really care.

She tugged at the zip on her dress and scrambled to the floor, her hand trembling a little as she smoothed her hair. Cormac fastened his shirt-buttons slowly, watching her with enigmatic eyes.

When Mrs Wendon knocked and entered to remove the tray, she found Lynda seated beside Cormac, while the television told its many tales of intrigue and passion before their watching eyes.

After she had gone, Cormac indicated to Lynda that

he wanted to stand. With her usual readiness, she helped him, hiding her disappointment at his intended absence from her side.

'I have work to do,' he informed her, withdrawn now, and back to the man across a desk.

'Do you want me to help you?' she asked hopefully.

'Stay here,' he replied, making for the door. 'You can tell me the end of the play.'

There was no opportunity to tell him about the play's end since Lynda did not see him again before she went to bed. Spending the night apart from Cormac in the smaller room held no attraction for her now. Even if he had no wish to touch her, it didn't matter. She wanted to feel him beside her, to know he was there.

Lying on her side, she found her whole body waiting for Cormac to come. Part of her wanted to slide into sleep, but the other part was obstinately refusing to give in. It seemed hours later when she became conscious of the movement of the bed, of someone beside her, a hand turning her and dragging her out of a dream.

'Lynda.' His voice was as taut as the muscles of the arms into which she was turned. 'I want you.'

Her mind was enveloped in a sleep-mist and she heard herself murmur, 'I want you, too, Cormac.' Her body, seemingly of its own volition, was pressing itself against him, her hands feeling for his shoulders.

'No.' He held her away. 'Too fast, lady. First, we take this lovely garment from between us.' He slipped her nightgown off and their dual nakedness was a combustible mixture. Her skin burned against his and she became supple and boneless in his embrace.

Already, his aroused state was making her throb and she wanted to feel his possession at once. Waiting was an agony and she tried to tell him. But her pleas made him laugh and she felt its distant thunder low down on his chest where her head was at that moment resting.

He pulled her up and her breasts, hard now with desire, felt the roughness of his chest hair arousing in her yet another exquisite sensation. His head bent and his mouth took control of her breasts, from one to the

other, until her head went back and her throat drank
gasps of air. His hand caressed her inner thighs and
made a way for himself between them for his complete
possession.

The joy of their total union did not stop, it went
rhythmically on and on until she cried out his name at
the height of her ecstasy, repeating it over and over on
the sun-flooded summit, hearing herself declare on the
leisurely downward journey, 'I love you, Cormac, I love
you so much.'

'I know, I know, my darling,' she heard him answer,
and in the bedlight's glow she saw his pleasure and the
total satisfaction he had gleaned from her rapturous
responses. In those golden moments, she believed he
meant the endearment and rejoiced in the fact. 'My
love, my own,' he was saying, kissing her throat, her
eyes, her lips, 'you drive me mad, you give me all I want
and more.'

Then he was still, his head beside hers on the pillow,
and they lay, still possessed of each other, while the
wild beat slowed to the soft throb of tranquillity.

It was so late when Lynda awoke, she heard from
downstairs the muffled movements of Mrs Wendon and
the sound of Jack Wendon's raised voice as they talked
while they worked. Lynda picked up her watch and
gasped at the time. As she pushed the covers back, she
saw her own state of undress and her heart raced as she
remembered the night's events. Cormac had left long
ago, it seemed, having managed somehow without her
help.

There was a note propped against an ornament
across the room. 'Stay home today,' it stated. 'Help
your mother move into the cottage. There's no need for
you to come to the office. Cormac.' It was the missing
word that made her sigh as she turned away.

Going downstairs twenty minutes later, she apologised to Mrs Wendon for being late for breakfast. 'It's
all right, Mrs Daly,' Mrs Wendon said, 'Mr Daly told
me not to cook you anything until you appeared. Said
you were tired after your hard day yesterday.'

Lynda nodded, wondering if she had imagined the twinkle in Mrs Wendon's eye. 'Any toast?' she asked. 'I'm not very hungry. Don't bother to cook anything.'

'Not even an egg, dear? If you're going to help your mum settle in,' the housekeeper advised, 'you'll need something better than just toast inside you.'

Lynda agreed on a poached egg on toast and coffee. 'Did my husband tell you about my mother coming today?' she asked as she made herself comfortable at the kitchen table.

'He did, dear. He thought she'd need your help. She's expected about eleven.'

'An hour's time?' Lynda started on her breakfast. 'I'd better hurry!'

Later, Lynda made her way across to the back door of the cottage. Mrs Wendon had told her that her husband, Jack, had already been there, opening windows to freshen up the place. It all looked so clean and tidy, it seemed that Mrs Wendon had been there, too.

The removal van lumbered along the narrow country lane as Lynda watched it through the front-room window. It pulled as close to the roadside as it could manage and Lynda wondered how long it would be before her mother arrived.

It was not one of the larger vans—her mother did not possess enough furniture to merit the use of one of those. The driver jumped down and went round to the other door, opening it and holding something in his arms, lifting an object down.

The 'object' he carried out was a small, determined lady who nodded and smiled sweetly at the burly man who had helped her.

'Mum!' Lynda cried, running out of the front door, and laughing with both pleasure and surprise. 'Trust you to cadge a lift along with your furniture!'

'Lynda dear,' Rose Groome kissed her daughter on both cheeks, 'you look wonderful!' She turned towards the van. 'The men had been so good, packing my things. When I told them my hands weren't all they might be, they told me my son-in-law,' she paused, the expression seeming to take her by surprise, 'my son-in-law had given instructions I wasn't to pack a thing, that they'd do it all.' She smiled beatifically at her daughter. 'You've got a wonderful husband, dear.'

Lynda smiled back. 'He's wonderful to you, Mother.'

'Why, isn't he to you, too, Lynda?'

Hurriedly, Lynda chased away her mother's puzzled frown. 'Wonderful, just great, Mum. In every way.' Well, isn't he? she asked herself sharply.

Two hours and a hurried lunch later, the removal van lumbered its way out of sight. Rose sank wearily into a chair, closing her eyes. Through the carefully made-up face, the slightly disordered hairstyle, Lynda observed with concern that the not-so-fit mother was creeping from hiding.

'Cup of tea, Mum?' she asked, getting to her feet.

As Rose nodded, there was a tap at the door and Mrs Wendon appeared, cups rattling on the loaded tray in her hands.

Eagerly, Rose sat up. 'My daughter must have "thought" you here,' she exclaimed to the smiling housekeeper. 'Just what I need.'

'Drink it down, Mrs Groome,' Mrs Wendon directed, handing the tray to Lynda. Her eyes roamed professionally. 'They've put the furniture in its place, but there's all those odds and ends to be put away. You'll need a hand with those. I'll get my Jack——'

'I'll help my mother,' Lynda intervened.

Rose shook her head. 'You've done enough, dear.'

'Jack will come over,' Mrs Wendon affirmed. 'You put your feet up, Mrs Daly.' To Rose, she said, 'Ten minutes, Mrs Groome?' Rose nodded gratefully and Mrs Wendon went away.

'I love it when she calls you Mrs Daly,' Rose mused, speaking the name with a mother's pride. 'I just can't see why wives object to being called by their husbands' surnames.' She smiled reflectively. 'In our day,' she was including her late husband, 'girls used to be proud of being married, and wearing that gold band. What's happened to girls, dear?' she asked her daughter with a sudden wide-eyed innocence.

Lynda laughed. 'Don't ask me, Mother.' She waved her wedding finger. 'I'm just a simple married woman.' Then she remembered telling Cormac that she thought it advisable to revert to her old name for business purposes. That, she argued silently, was because of her unusual situation in being both the wife of the chairman and a company employee. Then she surprised herself by saying, 'These days, women like to keep their identity. If you know what I mean,' she qualified.

'No, I don't, dear.' It was plain Rose's energies had started to revive, by the bright smile on her face. 'If you can tell me how a woman can be a wife and mother, plus a businesswoman—if that's what you mean by "identity"—and keep her health and contentment, then I'd be glad to hear it.' She inspected her own stiffening fingers. 'People push themselves too much these days. Once, it used to be the men. Now it's women, too.' She shook her head, still clearly not understanding.

Lynda sat down, then immediately stood up. 'I think I'll go to the——' Office, she had been going to say, but stopped guiltily after her mother's telling words. 'Pushing herself'—did her mother have a point, after all? Hadn't Cormac himself told her to take the day off? What neither her mother nor Cormac understood was the overwhelming tug she felt towards the place where her husband was at that moment spending his time.

'Go to the——?' Rose was saying. 'It's up those stairs, dear, turn right . . .'

Lynda burst out laughing. 'Not there, Mother. To—to——' The laughter still lingered in her throat. If only life were as simple as her mother seemed to think. A sigh eased from her lungs, only to be drowned by a rap at the door.

'Jack Wendon, Mrs Groome,' Jack announced, entering and holding out his hand. 'You go, Mrs Daly. I've got my wife's instructions, and one of them was to tell you to put your feet up.'

Rose laughed with her daughter. 'Your wife's trained you well, Mr Wendon,' she remarked, rising. 'Has she kept her identity, do you think?'

Jack intercepted the quick glance Rose gave her slightly startled daughter and smiled indulgently.

Back in the house, Lynda wandered restlessly. I'll go to work, she decided, unable to stand her own aimlessness. Having made the decision, she told a disapproving Mrs Wendon, who asked if she would like her husband Jack to run her to the station.

'I'll call a taxi. Will you tell my mother where I've gone?' The housekeeper nodded and Lynda went to the telephone.

As she approached Betty Peters' office, Lynda experienced a curious uprush of apprehension. How would Cormac greet her? Would he be angry, order her home, perhaps? Betty was with him, and it was she who showed surprise. Cormac merely raised an eyebrow, easing himself back in his seat to look her over. Lynda knew he would be seeing her neat blue dress which even he would surely be unable to fault. Whether he would also see through her poise to the underlying nervousness, she did not know.

As the secretary left, Cormac watched Lynda take her seat at her desk. Without preamble, he launched into work-talk. 'I contacted the man Colling. The Home-aid project is yours.' He pushed a folder across his desk.

Lynda's heart, already speeding at the mere sight of him, raced faster. She said, trying to decipher his words, 'I thought you were going to train me to be your personal assistant?'

'On thinking it over,' his eyes were slowly stripping her, to her dismay making her warm with desire instead of annoyance, 'I think you'd be wasted as a mere extension of me. You have a good brain. It should be used to inititate and organise, and not merely to develop other people's ideas.'

Slowly, she rose to accept the proffered folder. She recalled her earlier discussion with her mother and

could not suppress a smile. She might or might not have
wanted it, but an 'identity' was being forced upon her.
Whether it was her own identity, she had yet to
discover.

A hand reached out to grasp hers as she caught
hold of the folder. 'What's the joke?' Cormac
demanded.

Instantly, she had become sensitive to his touch, but
she managed to hide the fact with a smile. 'Just a
discussion I had today with my mother. She can't
understand modern woman.' Her blue eyes challenged
him. 'Can you?'

The ice that froze away the warmth from his features
made her shake with cold.

'I don't give that,' he clicked his fingers, 'for modern
woman.'

There was a distance between them now that she had
reached her desk, but she had to clarify his meaning.
'You're talking about your ex-fiancée?'

'I'm talking also,' his jaw thrust forward menacingly,
'about a certain *modern* woman who married me for the
money I could provide her with.'

Her eyes held his. 'It's not true,' she protested, 'but
even if it were, I'm working for my keep. I'm here, at
this desk, with this to tackle.' She held up the folder, as
yet thin in its contents. 'Doesn't that prove to you I'm
not as mercenary as you think I am?'

'If it proves anything,' he struck back, 'it's that
you're using your connection with me to gain
promotion.'

Lynda sprang up, standing stiffly. 'That's unfair! I
didn't ask to be upgraded, nor to have a desk in your
office. You—you wished them both on to me.' He
looked at her, unmoved. 'You're so determined to think
the worst of me, you can't see the trees for the wood—I
mean the wood for the . . .' She sank down, elbow on
desk holding her head, and hiding the filling of her eyes.
'Oh, you know what I mean,' she muttered.

The telephone rang on her desk. She looked up,
startled, inadvertently revealing the trickle of moisture

down her cheeks. 'How can that be for me? I'm not here this afternoon. Officially, I mean.'

Cormac saw the tear-streaks, but his manner did not soften. 'I told the man Colling to call you at half-past three.'

The ringing went on. 'You mean you guessed I'd come in?'

'I had a hunch.'

She didn't like his sardonic smile. 'Because I couldn't keep away from you, I suppose?' she remarked acidly. The sarcasm turned sour in her mouth, since it was the truth.

'Answer that damned thing, will you?' he snapped, returning to his work.

When the call was over, Lynda gazed at Cormac. His head was bent over a pile of correspondence. 'He wants me to go to the factory and see the dust extractor installed and working.'

Cormac did not look at her. 'I heard.'

She would *make* him lift his head. 'Did I handle it well?'

'As well as I expected.' He must have sensed her disappointment at his faint praise, because he looked at her. 'What the hell do you want me to say—that you're wonderful, you're the greatest find I've made in years?' His expression became personal. 'In one sense, that's true. If there's a woman who's got everything, it's you.'

Lynda flushed. 'You wouldn't have said that to a man.'

'A man wouldn't have demanded my praise or my acknowledgment of his ability to tackle a new marketing project.'

It was a put-down, but Lynda knew she had deserved it. She stood up, gathering the notes she had made and pushing them into the folder. It had started to grow thicker already, she noted with pleasure.

'Where are you going?' The grey eyes regarding her were cold.

'The appointment's for five o'clock. It will take me some time to get there.'

'Oh no,' he said with decision. 'There's no need at this stage for you to work after hours.'

'Mr Colling will be expecting me,' she said, dismayed.

'It goes without saying that he mentioned a meal afterwards?' he commented dryly.

'He mentioned the possibility of dinner if I was there longer than I expected.'

She heard the crash of a hand on his desk, saw him operate the intercom. 'Betty, cancel my wife's five o'clock appointment with the man Colling. Tell him she's just discovered she's got another one at that time. Make it for ten-thirty in the morning.'

Lynda stood up again. 'If I really am taking over this job,' she stormed, 'I'll do it my way, thanks. I'll make or break my own appointments!'

It was as though he had turned deaf, and that she had become invisible. Her anger hung upon the air in the hard silence. He had defeated her but, she fumed, I'll have my revenge.

As the hands of her watch reached five o'clock, she made for the door.

Cormac's hard voice followed her. 'You're coming home with me.'

'Thanks, but no. I'll find my own way there.'

'Lynda!'

Her body siffened as she became motionless. The command in his voice was not to be ignored.

'Help me to stand,' he demanded.

Still she wouldn't turn. 'You're getting more mobile. You don't need my help so much.'

There was no reply. Her muscles slackened, and her resistance collapsed. He needed her help. It was a need she did not have it in her to refuse to gratify. Nor ever would, she thought helplessly.

In a series of now familiar movements, she helped him to his feet. As she would have moved back, his arms went round her waist, holding her against him. His expression was grim. 'If there's any dining out on your schedule in the future, it will be with me and no one else. Got that?'

Compressing her lips, she nodded. Couldn't he ever be anything but angry with her? Wasn't there any gentleness in him where she was concerned?

'How about lunching out with a client?' she asked. 'Is that banned, too—except with you, of course.'

Her attempt at sarcasm drew a hard smile to his lips. 'Dinners are out, lunches are in. Okay, Mrs Daly?'

Her lips grew tremulous at his sudden change of mood. 'Okay, Mr Daly.' Her eyes smiled up at him. With a sudden movement, he lowered his head, taking a kiss. It was, she was certain, meant to be brief, but when he felt her hands move on his chest underneath his jacket, the kiss changed in character, parting her lips.

His free hand slid down her hip to her thigh and her mouth felt the persuasion of his exploring lips. In a movement that was both dismissing yet reluctant, he urged her away, breaking all contact.

They were driven home by Jack Wendon. As the car nosed through the evening rush-hour traffic, Cormac said, 'I take it your mother's settling in? No difficulties or hold-ups?'

Lynda was shaking her head when Jack remarked over his shoulder, car at a standstill near a road junction, 'She's doing fine, Mr Daly. I put out all her little knick-knacks and trinkets.' He drove on.

'That was good of you, Mr Wendon,' Lynda responded. 'She has so many miniature ornaments, she really needs a floor-to-ceiling glass-fronted cabinet to put them in!'

Jack laughed. 'She stood over me to make sure I didn't break any.'

'You want a cabinet for your mother?' Cormac asked the question briskly, bringing Lynda's head round. His face was expressionless—it might have been a business matter they were discussing.

'I didn't ask for one.'

'Maybe not in so many words. The request was implicit in the remark.' He flicked his eyes over her angry frown. 'At the weekend, you can go with her to choose one. It can be either antique or modern. Go to one of the London stores, if you like. Whatever it costs, I'll pay up.'

His faint smile said, That was why you married me, wasn't it? Lynda jerked her body round so that he did not even appear in her side vision.

Cormac made for the main living-room. With Lynda's assistance, he sank into a low chair. When he winced, her own leg suffered an empathetic, lightning shaft of pain sensation. That, she thought, is how much I love him. Yet if I tried to tell him he would laugh in disbelief.

'A drink?' she queried, hovering.

'You learn fast.'

'Same as usual?' She handed him the glass, finding a seat opposite him. She tried to avoid his eyes, but found her gaze drawn to his. He was appraising her as he drank, and she felt her skin prickle. Something was coming, something cynical, she was sure of that.

'If I judged your feeling for me by the way you come at my call, I'd be convinced you loved me.' His glass hit a low table.

So she had guessed right about his cynicism. Well, she would throw his taunt right back at him. 'It was part of our very own marriage contract, wasn't it?' she challenged. 'I'm helping you because it's what you pay me for.' She wondered if she would ever forgive herself for that untruth.

His mouth grew taut, but all he said was, 'We'll call on your mother after dinner.'

Mrs Wendon coughed and put her head round the door. 'Ten minutes, Mr and Mrs Daly,' she said. 'Don't let the food spoil now, will you?'

Cormac nodded and stretched out a hand to Lynda. At once she rose, giving him the assistance he needed.

Later, as they walked across the gardens to the rear door of the cottage, Lynda thought, Now he'll see my mother as she really is—off guard because she's not expecting us, showing just how incapacitated she really is.

Rose was busy in the tiny kitchen. She looked immaculate, as if she had spent an hour in front of the mirror. The pleasure she felt at their visit shone from her face. Of course she's taking care over her appearance, Lynda told herself, irritated by her own misjudgment of the situation. Here, where she's within calling distance of anyone from the big house, she would be on her guard every moment of the day.

It meant that Cormac might never see her with that guard down, which also meant that he would go on believing that she, Lynda, had made it all up.

Jack Wendon had been right in saying that her mother was doing fine. Her possessions had been few and the cottage ready for occupation. There was, even at that early stage, scarcely a thing out of place.

Showing them into the small living area, Rose urged them on to the settee, placing herself tidily on the gaily-patterned armchair. 'I'll never be able to thank you, Mr——' She paused at his frown, watching his mouth as it silently formed the syllables of his first name.

Smiling, she said, 'Cormac. And I'm Rose. I'm also your mother-in-law, of course.' The fact evoked a puzzled frown, as if she had still not worked out how it had happened that way.

'Of course.' Cormac's smile was gentle. 'And don't even try to thank me. This place was available, and I can't think of anyone better than my mother-in-law to occupy it.' He turned his head. 'The mother of my darling wife.' Only Lynda heard the false ring of the endearment. His hand covered hers, as if to emphasise his devotion to her.

'Your Mrs Wendon's been so good, Cormac,' Rose was saying. 'And Jack, her husband.'

'He was telling us,' Lynda put in, 'how careful you told him to be with your little ornaments.' She looked around her. 'I never knew you had so many. It must take you hours to dust them all!' Her head stayed rigidly sideways, where it had swept in its inspection. Even as she had said the words, she realised that

Cormac would have taken them as a signal to introduce the subject of a cabinet.

As his fingers tightened over hers, she knew he was communicating his angry acknowledgment of the supposed hint.

'Lynda suggests you could do with a display cabinet,' Cormac stated.

Rose took an excited breath, then expelled it. 'It's on my list of wanted things,' she agreed, 'but low down. I doubt if I'll ever really be able to afford one.'

'This coming weekend, Lynda will take you wherever you want and you can choose one together.' He smiled at his mother-in-law's astonishment. 'Antique or modern, it's your choice. A gift from me,' he glanced at his wife and seemed to enjoy her embarrassment, 'from us both.'

'Cormac,' Rose enthused, 'you really mean it? It's so good of you to——'

'Don't call me good, Rose,' he returned with the merest suggestion of sharpness. Then his smile came back. 'Let's call it a promise kept.'

'A promise?' Rose enquired, puzzled.

Lynda attempted to tear her hand from his, only to feel his fingers tighten still more.

Since Cormac seemed to have no intention of supplying the answer to the puzzle, Lynda filled in, 'The—the promise Cormac made to me in the car this evening when Mr Wendon told us about your ornaments.'

'He made you a promise to buy me a cabinet? Well, that was very thoughtful of you, Cormac. I can see it standing——' she looked around, 'there. No, over there. Antique, I think, mahogany or dark oak, or——' she looked uncertainly at her son-in-law '—would they be too expensive, Cormac?'

He smiled again, briefly, as if there was something on his mind. 'Money is no object, Rose.'

This time he allowed his wife to remove her hand with no difficulty at all.

Arriving back at the house, Cormac had told Lynda he

had work to do. He had looked at her as if waiting for her protest. There had been one on its way, but she had choked it back.

As he made his way, crutches in place, towards his study, she threw casually after him, 'I'll be glad of the peace and quiet. I'm going to look through the notes I took this afternoon about Home-aid's plans for their new product.'

He paused without turning, straightened his back, nodded and went on his way.

Now she sat, notes on her lap, idly turning the few pages the folder held. Mr Colling had emphasised on the telephone how anxious his company was to explore overseas markets. This she had written down, beside it, after the call, she had made a queried note, Surely home sales should be established first?

Putting aside the folder, she walked around the sitting-room. It was expert advice she required, the advice of Cormac Daly, and he sat working in another room only a few yards distant. He was her husband, yet he was still as remote from her as he had been the first time she had seen him at the door of that large, impersonal office.

Not only that, she thought. There's something inside me that refuses to let me go creeping to him for help. They talk about male pride. Well, I've discovered something and it's called *female* pride. I won't let him reduce me in size by telling me again that a man would have gone right ahead using his initiative and following his business instincts.

The phone rang. 'Lynda? Am I being a nuisance?'

'You're never that, Mother. Is there something you want?'

'Do forgive me, dear, but—but I was wondering if Cormac would mind . . . I don't know how to say it.'

Lynda heard the hesitation with some dismay. Was her mother taking Cormac at his word when he had stated that money was no object? Had she thought of some other expensive item she had set her heart on?

'My first night here,' Rose was saying. 'I'm just a

little nervous. Would Cormac object, do you think, if I asked you to come and sleep here in that tiny spare bedroom? I mean, if you don't want to, I understand . . .'

Lynda's relief at the simple request was profound. 'I'm sure he won't mind, Mum, and nor do I. I'll make up the bed——'

'I've seen to it, dear,' Rose answered cheerfully. Lynda smiled at her mother's assumption that her request would be granted. 'Come whenever you like, Lynda. No hurry. Just knowing you're coming will help me sleep.'

Lynda promised she would be over soon and went with no small amount of trepidation towards her husband's study. The door was ajar and he must have heard her coming, since he called out, 'Don't hover. Come in.' He looked up, irritation pleating his forehead.

Explaining the reason for her mother's call, Lynda waited for the explosion. There was none, only a brief lift of a shoulder. 'Go ahead, I can understand how your mother feels.'

'So you don't mind if I spend the night there?'

He threw down his pen. 'Of course I bloody well mind!'

'You mean you can't sleep without a woman in your bed?'

'I mean I can't sleep without you in my bed.'

Lynda's eyelids closed, then opened. She just had to be reading more into that statement than he intended! 'You—you mean you can't sleep without your fix of nightly sex?'

By the violence of his expression, she knew she had pushed him too far. 'By heaven, if my leg were normal, I'd be across there beating you senseless! Get out, Lynda,' he said with menace, 'or I'll have you down on that floor here and now, ravaging you until you beg for mercy.'

Lynda stood her ground, although her every instinct told her to run for cover. 'Will you be able to manage without my help?'

'Help, help, always *help*! Since when have I needed your assistance in undressing myself?' His glance narrowed reflectively. 'I'll bear that in mind ...' He withdrew his attention, thrusting her away mentally.

'Goodnight, then,' she said.

His frigid goodnight in reply chilled her through to her bones.

CHAPTER EIGHT

MORNING, to Lynda, seemed a long time coming. She had dreamed, at the rare times she had slept, of Cormac being beside her, holding her for love, instead of the lust he declared he felt for her.

Her mother rose first, calling her and getting her breakfast, saying how grateful she had been for her daughter's presence. 'I'll be fine on my own, now,' Rose had told Lynda.

Although she was early returning to the house, she found Cormac was already at work, having breakfasted. When she appeared at his study door, he looked up at her cursorily.

'You slept well, I see,' he commented, heavily sarcastic.

'I suppose you slept the night through?' she asked sweetly.

'Like hell I did.' He sat back, eyes on her face. 'I nearly came over and carried you back.' He made to get up and she went across to him at once, helping him.

His fist under her chin forced her to meet his eyes. 'Tonight, *I* want your company. Your mother must understand how it is.'

'My mother understands how it is—how she thinks it is between us.'

He looked as if he were about to say more, but moved away slowly.

The drive to the office was in silence. Jack whistled now and then as if he felt the need to break it. In the lift, Lynda stood by Cormac's side. His mood was bordering on the taciturn and Lynda wondered if she was the cause or whether his leg was bothering him more than usual.

In his office, she helped him into his chair before

taking hers at her desk. As she rooted in the Home-aid account folder, she felt he was watching her.

She knew she looked good in her neat grey suit, its colour sweetened by touches here and there of palest pink. They were echoed in the pink silk blouse she wore, with a flattering tie bow at the neck.

'You're blossoming,' with his succinct comment.

With a quick, impudent smile, she returned, 'Like a bride in bud?'

He did not smile back, but it was plain he was not unaffected by the mischief in her eyes by the way he growled, 'Into a full-blown businesswoman. For God's sake, don't get hard like so many of your liberated contemporaries.'

'By the time I do, your leg will be cured,' she replied, deliberately lifting her tone to lightness, 'and you'll have no more need of me for a wife.'

'What do you suggest I do—divorce you, then take you as my mistress?' His eyes glinted. 'Your financial circumstances would stay the same, so you would have no *money* worries.' He paused to see if the taunt had gone home. 'You would even be able to retain the use of my name.' The idea seemed to please him. 'On second thoughts, I could keep you as my wife and take on another woman as my——'

Lynda flung the folder down so hard on the desk, papers scattered. 'Will you stop——'

The phone on her desk rang, at which her husband laughed, head back. She gave him a killing look which made him laugh louder.

'Just reminding you, Mrs Daly, of your appointment,' said Betty Peters. 'Almost time you were leaving.'

'Thanks a lot, Betty,' Lynda answered, ringing off.

Without a word, she collected everything she needed for the meeting with Mr Colling. She would go to the door as if Cormac was not there . . .

One of his crutches caught her eye as she turned to go. She heard herself say, 'Will you be able to manage?'

'Without you?' His voice was hard now. 'As well as I did before I met you.'

He had meant to hurt her, but she hid her pain with a businesslike nod and swung to the door.

It was mid-afternoon before she returned to the office. Mr Daly was at a meeting, Betty Peters informed her, but he shouldn't be long now. Lynda nodded, saying she had plenty of work to be getting on with.

It was an hour later when Cormac swung into the room. He had been talking for some time in the corridor outside and the sound of his voice had started Lynda's emotions spinning. She was still aware of the warmth in her features which had been put there by the fast pace of the discussion at her meeting with Donald Colling, and by the meal she had eaten with him in the visitors' section of the senior staff dining-room.

Cormac gave her a skating glance as he made his way to his desk. 'Expense account lunches agree with you,' he commented dryly. 'I know of only one other activity that puts that kind of warmth in your cheeks.'

Her colour deepened at his comment as she walked across to give her usual assistance, but it seemed he was increasingly able to help himself. As she retreated to her desk, the fact depressed her rather than pleased her. The lessening of his dependence on her brought that much nearer the end of their marriage.

'So what did Home-aid Planners have to say?' he asked.

'They want the product of the small company they've just acquired marketed in any country in the world who'll take it on board.'

'Domestic dust extractor? You'll have to advise them to curb their enthusiasm in the initial stages. There are limited markets for such a commodity until it has proved itself.'

Lynda nodded, consulting her notes. 'I suggested they should concentrate on the home market first.'

'And did your friend Colling agree with your advice?'

'It took a bit of persuasion on my part. Donald's young and enthusiastic and——'

'Donald?'

'Donald,' she stated firmly. 'Donald Colling.' She

saw her husband's narrowed stare and went on
defensively, 'He told me to use his first name.' Cormac's
gaze did not waver and she felt annoyance rising. 'If I'd
been a man you wouldn't be objecting to that. It's
usually considered good business, isn't it—informality,
a breaking down of conventional barriers?'

'Not where my wife's concerned.'

'But I'm not your wife——' A muscle moved in his
cheek. 'Oh, of course I am, but surely you know what I
mean?'

'The only man who is going to break down your
barriers, Lynda, is myself.'

She took a steadying breath, and let it out slowly.
Grasping a pencil and stabbing her notepad with it, she
said, 'If I'm to continue with this job you've given me, I
think I shall have to move out of your office. In here,
I'm just an extension of your personality. No matter
how hard I try to break free, you won't let me. Either
that or,' she took a second breath, wavering this time, 'I
shall have to find myself a job with another company.'

'Is that an ultimatum?'

'I'm not being emotive, Cormac, merely factual,
pragmatic, if you like.' His face had become unreadable
and she could no longer guess which way he would
jump. The whole situation was unnerving, throwing her
thought processes into confusion. She had to go on now
that she had started. 'Being in here inhibits me. If I had
an office of my own——' she nodded towards the
adjoining room 'that office—I'd feel freer to use my
initiative without feeling I had to defer to you all the
time.'

'Right. Move out of here.'

She felt as if he had taken the chair from under her.
She had been geared up to do emotional battle, but he
had treated her challenge with contempt. Worse, he had
turned the tables and was ordering her out.

Gathering her injured pride together with any
portable pieces of equipment she could lay her hands
on, she walked through into the smaller office. Cormac
watched her go without a word.

As she went to close the door, the telephone rang on her old desk. Depositing the items she was carrying in the smaller office, she hurried back and lifted the receiver.

'Is that Miss Groome? Lynda Groome?' the caller asked.

'Lynda Groome speaking. Good afternoon, Don——' She felt Cormac's displeasure reaching out, 'Mr Colling.'

Lynda could almost feel the man at the other end of the line blush, his red hair springing spikily. 'Please make it Donald. We agreed on first names, Lynda. You no doubt recall, Lynda, that I'm most anxious to get this new product of ours not only advertised in the press, but also to have the media's active interest in it.'

'Yes, I do remember that, Donald.' She closed her mind to Cormac's noisy movements. 'We agreed on the name—Dustractor, wasn't it?'

'Yes, yes,' Donald Colling agreed eagerly. 'We also decided to catch the attention of busy housewives and mothers, the people who will benefit most from its installation.'

'Saving them the job of constant dusting.'

'Right.' His eagerness seemed to be increasing. 'I was wondering, Lynda, whether yóu would consent . . .' He seemed to be experiencing difficulty in expressing himself. 'It's just that I've seen another piece of advertising matter put out by the company you work for—Kitchenware by Brightling. The girl in the ad might almost be you.'

Lynda managed an exclamation of surprise.

'It occurred to me as I looked at it that you might——' he seemed to have some momentary trouble in breathing '—with your looks and warmth, you might well represent the epitome of the young housewife and mother.' He paused, as if holding his breath for her response.

Doodling madly on a scrap of paper with a spare pencil, she offered, colour deepening, 'I really don't think, Donald, that I could possibly——'

'Oh, I know you aren't married, but you have the look of a woman who could be . . .' He appeared to realise the tangle into which he was talking himself. Maybe, Lynda thought wryly, he had remembered the unconventional times in which he was living. 'You could be,' he repeated. 'We could put a ring on your finger . . .'

Lynda became appalled at how far his thoughts had advanced on the subject and wished with all her heart that she had told him who she really was.

Firmly, she said, 'I'm flattered by your suggestion, Donald, but I really couldn't pose for a photograph. I'm not a trained model, I couldn't possibly accept a fee——'

'You surprise me,' a voice cracked out from across the office.

'But this Kitchenware ad,' Donald persisted, 'the girl could be you in every way.'

Silently, Lynda cursed Larry Chapman for having involved her in the first place. If it hadn't been for that picture . . . her eyes flickered shut. So many things wouldn't have happened. The man over there behind that desk would not now be her husband, she would never have known his lovemaking . . .

'I'm sorry, Mr Colling,' she declared, reverting to formality in the hope of re-establishing her position as a marketing executive—however much of a novice she might be in that field. 'But I'll do my best to find a model who has the necessary looks and personality. I'll put you through to Rodge Miller, our studio manager. Will you hold while I transfer your call?'

Sighing, Lynda closed her eyes. Would that photograph she posed for never fade from her life, never stop affecting it?

'So you aren't married?' Cormac's voice came at her like a buffeting wave.

'I told you I thought it best for business reasons to call myself Groome instead of Daly.'

'There are other ways of knowing whether a woman is married.' His eyes flashed red for danger. 'What did you do with your rings?'

'Transferred them to my other hand.'

There was an ominous pause. Lynda doodled madly, drawing zigzag lines, pressing into the paper and tearing it. Her head lifted and a shock jagged through her at the fury in his eyes. 'Are you going to two-time me like that ex-fiancée of mine?'

Lynda swallowed, feeling the tears threaten. 'I'd never do that to you, Cormac,' she answered steadily.

'Of course you wouldn't. You'd have too much to lose, like all that cash tied up in our marriage deal.'

There was simply no answer to his constant allegations of self-interest.

As she rose to go, the telephone sounded on Cormac's desk and she slipped away into her new office.

During dinner that evening, Cormac told her he would be leaving next day to attend a conference in Manchester. Lynda put down her knife and fork and took a drink of water.

'Do you want me to go with you? To help with your work, I mean, or your leg . . .?'

'Thanks, but no. My work will be dealt with by the administrative assistance provided. My leg,' his shoulders lifted. 'I'm more than capable of looking after myself when necessary these days—or hadn't you noticed?'

Only too well, she thought, wishing the water she had drunk had for once been something stronger. 'You mean it involves an overnight stay?'

'In my diary, it spans five consecutive days. I shall be coming back late on Monday. On the Sunday there are a number of planned visits. I doubt if I shall go, but there's an important final meeting on the Monday morning.'

Four nights without him, five empty days to get through? Lynda stared at him, uncaring that he might see her thoughts reflected in her eyes.

'Are you trying to tell me you'll miss me?' The idea seemed to amuse him.

'Miss you? Of course I won't miss you!' She resumed

eating, hoping she gave every indication of being hungry. Searching unsuccessfully for a follow-up remark, she gave up battling with the food and pushed her half-empty plate away.

'Yes,' she whispered, making no attempt this time to mask her unhappiness, 'I'm sorry, but I will.' Pushing back her hair, she prepared to leave.

'Don't run away from the inevitable, Lynda.'

'What inevitable?' she asked bitterly. 'That I should fall in love with a man who only uses me to assuage his sexual appetite? In my book, respect goes hand in hand with love. How can I respect a man who only uses me?' To her relief, she had managed to control the quiver in her voice.

It was necessary to pass him to reach the door. His hand caught hers. 'So you neither love me nor respect me?'

Her lips felt parched. 'I——'

'Which makes you no better, *in your book*, than you allege I am.'

'But I don't use *you*,' she protested, trying to free her hand.

'You don't? What's sharing my house and my bed, if not that? What's accepting the frequent injections of cash I make into your bank balance, if not using me?'

'Leave me alone!' she exclaimed, and found he had freed her hand.

'Gladly.' He pulled himself to his feet and Lynda quelled her instinct to help him. 'I have work to do for the conference. Do you want to ask your mother over to keep you company?'

His icy tone made her go cold, but she answered composedly, 'No, thank you. I'll go to her cottage. The atmosphere's warmer there. And at least she'll be pleased to see me.' She cursed the waver in her voice. Had there been the faintest glimmer of a response in Cormac's face? But he had turned away, and she would never know.

Rose chatted to her daughter for most of the evening.

Lynda enjoyed the time she spent at her mother's cottage, even if occasionally her mind was not completely on the conversation.

Her thoughts strayed with frightening frequency to Cormac, to his coming absence, to wondering how long it would be before he told her he didn't need her any longer in his life.

There was the sound of music as she let herself into the house. She traced it to the other living-room she had found the day she had explored the place.

Cormac was lounging on a couch, legs extended, shirt partly unbuttoned, eyes closed. If I hadn't known his leg was injured, Lynda thought, entering quietly, I would never have guessed. He did not open his eyes even when she sat beside him. She could have chosen another chair, but his tug on her senses was such that she felt as if he were compelling her to his side.

Letting the music take over, she relaxed, closing her eyes and forcing her hand not to touch him. When his hand came out to take hers, the nerves in her body jumped for joy.

'You're too far away,' Cormac growled. 'Come closer. No, closer still.'

He was not satisfied until she was half-lying on him, his arm around her and her cheek against his chest. Her lips found their way to rest on his shirt. He tolerated it for a moment, then, with his free hand, he tugged his shirt fully open and pressed her head against the bareness of his chest.

The music seemed to be working a magic spell, softening his unforgiving attitude towards her. 'Kiss me,' he said gruffly, impelling her lips round until they made contact with his skin. Intoxicated by the cadences and harmonies which filled the air, she gave way to her instincts and placed small kisses over the taut flesh, the rough hair that partially covered it and, venturing lower, the hard leanness of his waist.

He caught her armpits and jerked her up. Pulling off her blouse and bra, he returned her kisses all over her sensitised skin. Then he shifted and she rolled beside

him. She saw the passion in his face, held her breath at
the feathering touch of his venturing hands and heard
him say:

'Go up. I'll follow.'

Clambering over him, Lynda collected her clothes,
holding them to her, feeling glad as she ran up the stairs
that the housekeeper and her husband had gone home.
Dashing into the shower, she rejoiced in the refreshing
cascade, feeling cleansed and glowing as she dried
herself.

Cormac was there before all the dampness had gone,
leaning against the bathroom's entrance and pulling
free of his clothes. He advanced towards her, taking his
weight on his injured leg with the merest trace of pain
around his mouth.

He removed the towel from her hands and pulled her
with him to stand under the shower. She shrieked and
laughed and tried to tell him she had already been there
and gone.

He laughed at her laughter, holding her against him,
letting her feel his state of arousal, tipping back her face
so that the force of the tepid water spattered over her
gasping features. Her hands groped for him, finding his
rib cage and digging in her nails in her abandonment to
pleasure.

He lifted her and swung her astride his hips, grasping
her thighs. Her fingers gripped his shoulders and
slipped. She felt herself falling backwards and she
shrieked again, this time in fear. He reached out to catch
her and pulled her back, and her cheek rested against
his shoulder as she breathed hard to steady herself.

The water ceased to run and they remained there,
intimately entwined, his mouth making free of her
body. She had never known such joy as coursed
through her at the contact, at the sensation of strength
that came from his supporting hands which held her
with the utmost intimacy.

Cormac limped with her to the bedroom, lowering her
to the fur rug near the bed. He lay beside her, swinging her
across him, and taught her to love him, pleasuring herself

at the same time as she pleasured him.

He urged her forward, licking the droplets from her silky skin, savouring most those on her burgeoning breasts. He moved her yet again, so that his weight was on her. She arched beneath him, smelt the cleanliness of his body and rubbed her face against the sheen of moisture left by the shower and mixed with the perspiration of his passion.

His hands and mouth, sometimes cruel, sometimes tender, had taken possession of her willpower, yet encouraged her to give free reign to all of her locked-in desires, stroking and caressing him and crying out her joy.

When she felt she had given to him everything possible of herself, he eased a pathway into her, showing her that even greater shared delights lay ahead, more than she had ever known.

Locked together in mouth and body for seemingly aeons of time, all thought evaporated, leaving behind a crystalline rapture which resolved itself into a rhythmic throb which took her to the stars.

All that was left of him next morning was the damp towel in the bathroom, his discarded clothes left for the housekeeper to collect.

He had left more of himself, Lynda luxuriated, than material possessions. In the night he had claimed her again, and they had merged together a second time, loath to part even when the slow descent into a radiant tranquillity had been achieved.

Still she could feel his kisses, on her mouth, on her body. Without much effort, she could summon up the feel of his hands all over her... Stirring, she realised it was so late she would have to miss her breakfast. Being the wife of the man in charge would not change her determination to work regular office hours.

Lynda had not been long at her desk when Rodge Miller called from his studio office.

'How's Mrs Cormac Daly this morning?' he asked. 'Has she tamed her husband's temper yet?'

Lynda laughed. 'She's fine, Rodge. And,' with mock innocence, 'whose temper were you referring to?'

Rodge laughed this time. 'Full of it this morning, aren't you? And you with an absent husband.'

'You knew Cormac had gone to a conference?'

'I knew.' There was a short, charged pause, then he came back with, 'I am one of the family, you know.'

A doubt had crept into Lynda's mind. 'He—he has gone to Manchester to a conference, hasn't he, Rodge?'

'Oh, yes, I can assure you of that. Ask Betty Peters. But that wasn't what I called you for. There's another account, or maybe I should have said another branch of the original. Kitchenware by Brightlings want to develop another idea. Housewife at Leisure. How does that grab you?'

'Show me a housewife, first, who has any leisure.'

'Ouch! Okay, so I ring back and tell them to stunt the branch before it sprouts. They're barking up the wrong tree.'

Lynda laughed at his imagery.

'Des Brown of Marketing seemed to think you'd had contact with Kitchenware in the past?' Rodge mentioned in a querying tone.

'Contact with Kitchenware?' Not that photograph, he hadn't meant that photograph? 'I didn't have the contact, Rodge. That was in Larry Chapman's time.' To her relief, he dropped the subject.

At lunchtime, she made her way to the staff restaurant, seeking out Mandy. Greeting Lynda happily, Mandy said, 'I don't know why you keep coming here, when you could go to some exotic restaurant with your husband.'

Lynda shook her head, taking a seat. 'Anyway, he's away for a few days.'

There was a scraping of a chair and Mandy's face began to turn pink. Lynda followed her eyes. 'Hi, Rodge. Nice to see you.' He nodded absently, his eyes were already on her companion.

'Rodge, you remember Mandy? At the—my—wedding?'

'Fairley five-four-eight-two. Right?'

Mandy's small face shone with pleasure. 'You remembered my phone number!'

Rodge grinned. 'Think I'd forgotten? I had to get the dust of one woman off my hands before I so much as looked at another.'

'Are your hands dust-free now?' Mandy joked.

He deposited his tray and held up his palms. 'Cleansed of all contamination. Now, how about a date?'

Mandy grinned. 'Bet you don't even remember my name.'

Lynda, intrigued, looked from one to the other.

'Amanda Ash. How's that? Do I merit a date now?' Rodge put up his hands in a begging fashion, making his audience of two laugh.

'How long,' Mandy asked, 'before I become "dust" to be brushed off your hands?'

'Hey, that was below the belt, Mandy. It takes a while to trust another woman when one's let you down. Ask Lynda about Cor——' He checked himself. 'I only asked for a date, not an orgy.'

Again, his companions laughed. Mandy looked at Rodge, awaiting his next move.

'Doing anything tonight?' he asked. 'Now, if you say you're washing your hair . . .'

'I—er—was thinking of going for a walk in the park.' She looked at him sideways. 'You could come with me, if you like.'

'Name the time and place.' Mandy did and they smiled at each other.

It was all so simple and straightforward, Lynda thought. Her relationship with Cormac was so much more complex, her future with him so much in doubt, she sighed. It was not even heard by her companions.

That evening, Lynda phoned her mother, inviting her to share her meal. Rose firmly refused her daughter's invitation. 'You come over to me, dear. I like the simplicity of my little cottage too much to leave it for the grandeur of your house.'

Lynda almost replied that it was not her house. Well, it wasn't, was it? she thought. I'm just a ship passing in the night, as they say. Then the thought of night filled her with an aching longing.

The Wendons had gone by the time she returned to Whitegates. The phone was ringing and Lynda raced to answer it. It just had to be Cormac.

'Hi, Lynda. Rodge.' Lynda's heartbeats slowed to normal. 'Before I go to meet Mandy, tell me something, will you? Is there a male in her life? A current boy-friend, partner, lover, flat-sharer——?'

Lynda laughed. 'You've forgotten fiancé and husband.'

'Oh, hell, there isn't is there?'

'Find out for yourself, Rodge,' Lynda teased. Then she became serious. 'I know you've been hurt, so I'll tell you. As far as I know, there isn't anyone at present. She wouldn't have asked you to tag along with her in the park tonight if there had been, would she? Some girls might, but she's not like that.'

There was a huge sigh in Lynda's ear. 'Thanks, pal.'

'Rodge,' Lynda asked a question that had been niggling at her mind all day, 'when I seemed surprised this morning that you knew Cormac had gone to a conference, you sounded a bit strange. Why, Rodge?'

There was a short silence, then Rodge said awkwardly, 'Do you really want to know?' He sighed. 'Okay. I thought you'd know that Yolande Wilson would be there, too.'

Lynda said hoarsely, 'Cormac's ex-fiancée?'

'Right. She's a public relations person for a textile firm—not one of ours. She changed her line, because she used to be a model. Worked for Daly Enterprises for a long time.'

'Which is how Cormac met her?'

'Right again. Hey, don't let it worry you, Lynda. You're his wife. He wouldn't go back to her, not after you. She's like used goods by comparison.'

'All the same,' Lynda answered unhappily, 'he proposed marriage to her. Rodge,' she asked slowly, 'how did she two-time him?'

Another pause, then Rodge supplied, 'That's another story. Ask Cormac some time.. Okay? 'Bye.'

Lynda dropped the phone as if it had burnt her. So last night's passionate coming together, the moments when Cormac had held her as if she were really part of him, had meant no more to him, after all, than a night of fulfilled male desire preparatory to a few nights of abstinence.

She told herself that Cormac would not call, and when the phone did ring, Lynda did not believe her ears. It persisted and she had to run from the bathroom to the bedroom extension. Lifting the receiver, she said breathlessly,

'Lynda Groome—I mean, Lynda Daly here.'

'I see,' the feminine voice drawled. 'Are you sure your name is Daly, *Mrs* Daly?'

'This is Lynda Daly speaking,' Lynda answered firmly. 'Who is——?' She knew who it was!

'So it's true. When Cormac told me this evening that he'd got married, I didn't believe him. What were you when he picked you up off the floor? Some little second-rate model?'

'I have heard, Miss Wilson,' Lynda retorted, 'that that's precisely what you were when Cormac chose you from——' she paused, thinking, I'll give this insolent female something to remember *Mrs Daly* by '—when he selected you from an identity parade. From the sound of it, the other girls in the line must have been really terrible for him to have chosen you.'

The phone slamming down hurt her ear. It was just as well, she thought, that Yolande Wilson couldn't see the trembling of her hands as she sank on to the bed. So Cormac had been discussing her with his ex-fiancée . . . Just where did that leave her? Right there, sitting alone on the bed they had shared so pleasurably—and, as she had thought, lovingly—only twenty-four hours ago.

Since there was nothing else to do, she got into bed, but she could not sleep for the tormenting thoughts that spun like a top in her brain. Cormac had never stopped loving Yolande Wilson. If he had, why hadn't he

removed that photograph of her which she herself had
found that first night beside the bed?

Where was that photograph now? Scrambling out,
she put aside her scruples and opened the first of
Cormac's drawers. It was in the third drawer she pulled
open, face upwards so that he could snatch a glance at
that sophisticated body, the beautiful face, without his
wife's knowledge.

The phone rang again, and she pushed the picture
back as if it had scorched her fingers. Her hand still
held a tremor of anger when she lifted the receiver.
'Yes?' she asked, uncaring if the caller heard the
sharpness.

'Lynda.' The curtness almost cut her ear. 'Where the
hell have you been all evening?'

'At my mother's for part of the time,' she answered
tensely. 'Why?'

'This is the fifth time I've tried to contact you. Twice
there was no reply, then the line was engaged.'

'Oh,' she answered, gritting her teeth, 'that was when
my secret lover called me, but thanks for your
persistence.' She thrust the receiver back on to its
cradle, trying to swallow the tears.

When it rang once more, she stared at it without
moving. The ringing stopped, then started again. This
time she answered.

'Now tell me who it really was.' It was a short, sharp
order.

'I phoned my mother. Then,' she paused to steady
her breathing, 'it was *your* lover, Yolande Wilson.'

The silence was so long, she wondered if he had gone.
She had to say a word, something to soften the anger
that hurtled across the distance that separated them. . . .
There was a click, then dead silence. Cormac had gone.
They had parted on a quarrel and now she wouldn't
sleep the whole night through.

CHAPTER NINE

THE telephone rang on her desk next morning, making her want to scream. She had woken, heavy-eyed from the few hours restless sleep she had had that night, with an aching head and a pain somewhere under her ribs.

'Hi, Lynda.' The voice was familiar, but she couldn't place it. 'Remember me? Larry—Larry Chapman?'

Oh no, she thought, haven't I got enough on my plate without another tasteless helping being added to it?

'How could I forget you, Larry?' she answered with sarcasm.

'You owe me a lot, *Mrs* Daly,' Larry shot back gloatingly. 'If I hadn't used my trained eye and chosen you to bring pots and pans to life, you wouldn't be Cormac Daly's wife. Now be honest, would you?'

Lynda found herself smiling but with reluctance. 'So what do you want, Larry? Knowing what I do of you, you wouldn't be calling me just to say "hello".'

'Is that how you think of me, Mrs Daly?' The way he said the name was an insolence in itself. 'I've started my own business. It's going to succeed. Isn't that a good enough reason to want to talk to you?'

Lynda waited, saying nothing.

'I've had a call from my successor as studio manager. Rodge—Rodge Miller. Know him?'

'Heard of him,' Lynda answered non-committally.

'Surprised you've only heard, since he seems to know you well enough. Daly's cousin, isn't he?'

Lynda took exception to Larry's growing impudence. '*Mister* Daly to you, Larry. Tell me,' her tone grew silky, 'rumour has it that you left to work for a rival company. What happened, did they throw you out, too?'

'Asking for trouble, aren't you, Mrs Daly?' His tone

had a sheen on it, too. 'If you must know, it was more profitable for me to form my own company instead of working for someone else. This way, I can control my own take-home pay, if you get my meaning?'

'Why did you ring me, Larry?'

'Kitchenware—remember? Rodge Miller told me they want to find the model who posed for that photograph. How about it, Lynda?'

'How about what, Larry?' Why did her toes begin to curl in apprehension? What could Larry Chapman do to her now? She was Cormac's wife, fireproof, surely, from Larry's devious schemes?

'Posing for me. There'd be a fat fee, Lynda. I'd argue for it on your behalf. They specially want that girl—you—so the sky's the limit as far as the price of you is concerned.'

'The "price of me," Larry,' Lynda pretended to joke, 'what a tactful way to put it!'

'But I thought every woman had her price. That's what they say, isn't?' Lynda clutched her pencil. 'You married the right man, didn't you? Don't try and kid me. I bet he's not as mean with you nowadays as he was that day he caught you modelling for me after you'd been fired. I bet,' there was a lip-licking pause, 'you get any fee you ask from him now you share his bed.'

Lynda rammed the receiver back into place and nursed her aching head. Last night, Yolande. This morning, Larry Chapman. Things usually come in threes, she thought. Who would be the next to torment her?

Seeking Rodge at lunchtime, she knew by feminine instinct that if she found Mandy, she would find Rodge. They were together, holding hands secretively under the table-top. So it had got that far, Lynda thought, aware of an ache inside her which she recognised as envy. Their coming together had been almost as fast as her own with Cormac, but with how much more genuine affection. . .

Taking a sandwich and coffee across the restaurant, Lynda said, 'I know I'm not welcome, but——' They were profuse in their assurances that she certainly was. 'Rodge, could I see you after work—have a coffee somewhere? Or,' with a glance at Mandy, 'would you be dating someone called Miss Ash?'

There was laughter and Mandy withdrew her hand from Rodge's, waving him towards Lynda. 'I can trust my best friend with her husband's cousin. We weren't dating tonight anyway,' she explained. 'I'm washing my hair,' with a grin at Rodge, 'and that's the truth.'

For a while, they talked generally, then Lynda, having eaten her small meal, left them. Rodge came for her after work, taking her to a local pub. Businessmen were gathered at the bar, taking a drink before hurling themselves into the rush-hour maelstrom. They laughed and joked the day's tension from themselves, business ties loosened, jackets removed, their professional masks being nudged away by the re-emergence of their human faces.

Lynda thought, seated at a table while Rodge bought the drinks, Haven't I seen Cormac's humanity, haven't I seen him laugh, eyes warm, business bonds abandoned, giving place to everyday domesticity? Haven't I? She shook her head, pushing around her beer mat, and sighing. Only in the course of their lovemaking had she had a glimpse of the real man. Or was it? She did not have sufficient knowledge of him to supply the answer.

A sherry appeared in front of her. 'There's something bugging you,' Rodge commented, sitting opposite her and swilling down his frothing beer.

Lynda took a sip or two, then put down her glass. Abruptly, she told him about Yolande's late-evening phone call. 'There are things I don't know,' she told him.

'I'll help if I can,' he promised, having expressed his condemnation of Yolande's behaviour.

'When you were explaining to Mandy about it taking a while for a man to trust a woman after a let-down, you said, "Ask Lynda about Cormac." I'm asking you about Cormac, Rodge.'

He studied the froth which still clung to the inside of the empty glass.

'One day, Cormac asked me,' Lynda went on, 'if I was going to two-time him like his ex-fiancée. Tell me what happened between them, please,' she begged, a hand on his arm.

He lifted a shoulder. 'If you insist.' He raised his glass. 'Mind if I get a refill? You, too?' She shook her head, and he was back in a few minutes. The bar had now started to empty of homebound businessmen. Rodge took his time about his first swallow. 'They were on a skiing holiday together.'

'Cormac and Yolande?'

'Right. Last January, in Switzerland. There's not much to it, really. It was getting dark and Yolande, against advice, spurted off alone down a slope.'

'She had an accident,' Lynda put in, 'and Cormac went after her—he told me that much.'

Rodge nodded. 'She fell heavily. What he didn't know was that another guy was watching Yolande's progress at the same time. He came out of the shadows and went speeding to her rescue, too.'

'He and Cormac collided?'

'Right again. They hit each other as Cormac slewed round to stop in front of Yolande.'

'Which is when he damaged his leg?'

Rodge nodded. 'As he lay there unable to help himself, he was forced to watch his beloved fiancée lift her arms to the other guy—who wasn't hurt by the collision—and see her carried off in his arms.'

'Someone came to help Cormac?'

'A crowd of them. They said how sorry they were, and they didn't just mean about his accident.'

'All of which made him take a dislike to women—and swear to have his revenge?'

'Give 'em hell, as I told you he said.'

'And one in particular? Would any woman do?'

He could see the way her thoughts were moving. 'Hey, Lynda, that wasn't why my cousin married you. One's only got to look at you to know that.'

Lynda smiled faintly. She knew a great deal that he didn't, but she was certainly not going to tell him.

'Yolande was having an affair with the guy who rescued her,' he went on.

'You mean while she was engaged to Cormac?'

Rodge nodded. 'It all added fuel to his fire, you might say. He's never forgiven her.'

'Or any woman,' Lynda stated flatly, understanding a great deal more now that she knew the full story.

'Yolande's still living with the other bloke,' Rodge added, finishing his beer. 'Okay? Don't look so miserable,' he comforted, rising with Lynda. 'You're Cormac's wife.'

'Only for as long as he needs my physical help, Rodge. When his leg's recovered completely, it's——' she ran her hand sideways across her throat '—that for me. Goodnight, Rodge. Thanks for coming.'

She left him staring after her.

The weekend seemed twice its normal length, and Lynda spent most of it with her mother. If Rose wondered at her daughter's strange preoccupation, the sad look in her normally bright eyes, she did not comment.

Together, they went into London, to one of the large, famous stores. Since Cormac had implied that money was no object, Lynda directed her mother to one of the best known. Rose wandered round the soft-carpeted, delicately lighted, imposingly spacious floors as if she were in a palace furnished by a rub of Aladdin's lamp.

Seeing the prices, Rose gasped, turning away and shaking her head. 'Don't worry, Mother,' Lynda said. 'Cormac's paying, whatever the cost—he said so. Just choose the cabinet you really want and don't even glance at the price-tag.'

'Well, dear,' resignation to the undreamed-of opportunity came swiftly, 'it's really a choice between that one, and——' she looked around, '—that one. And I think it will be,' a swift examination followed, 'that one.'

Lynda nodded, smiling secretly. It was, she discovered, almost the most expensive of that type of cabinet in the store. 'You have good taste, Mother,' she commented wryly. Rose took it as an enormous compliment, smiling happily.

Travelling home, Rose seemed wrapped around with delight at her purchase. Lynda was glad, since it left her to her own thoughts, although they did not make pleasant travelling companions. The next two nights she spent at her mother's place. For the last two nights, she had discovered how cold and wilderness-like a double bed was when only one person occupied it.

Monday came finally, the day of Cormac's return. Lynda forced her excitement to a low level, but as the morning went by, she felt her control of it slipping. It was after lunch that Betty Peters entered her office agitatedly.

'There's someone to see you, Mrs Daly. I think I should warn you, she's——'

'Warn Mrs Daly of what, Mrs Peters?' The slim, sophisticated woman who came in was instantly recognisable. Lynda had seen the face before, in that provocative photograph which had stood on the table in Cormac's bedroom.

The surface enticements were there in plenty—style, shape and bold brown eyes. The grey suit she wore did not hide the promise implicit in the body beneath it, the black silk blouse, frilled high to frame the perfectly-featured face, a daring challenge to the suit's unexciting colour.

Betty withdrew as though with reluctance. She needn't worry, Lynda thought. I could hold my own against a dozen women like this. Or so she believed until Yolande Wilson started speaking.

'Maybe Betty was going to warn you about the effect I still have on your husband's reflexes—to put it just a little crudely, Mrs Daly.' She occupied a chair as if honouring the simple, straight-backed piece of office furniture with her presence.

'Reflexes of self-preservation, do you mean?' Lynda

asked conversationally, the sarcasm being made all the more effective by her manner. 'The age-old instincts of once bitten, never to touch again?'

The brown eyes blazed. 'You're so wrong, Mrs Daly. The reflexes I'm talking about are those that have stopped the human race from dying out. Like a man longing to touch and make love to a warm, familiar body. In case you're missing the point, mine to Cormac. Do you know how very *familiar* we two were, *Mrs Daly*?' She managed to turn the name into an insult.

'Let me guess,' answered Lynda, managing a smile.

This time the barb made no impression on her visitor. Instead, the brown eyes turned on Lynda with a look of pity. 'I'm sorry for you, really. Your marriage to Cormac has been too short for you to get to know him, hasn't it?'

'I know he's never forgiven you.' To Lynda, the ground seemed somehow to be slipping from under her feet, like a skier heading for disaster.

'And don't you think that might imply that he's never really stopped loving me?' The long, elegant legs crossed, the trim figure settled more comfortably.

Lynda's only defence was to glance at her watch and make a definitive movement as if her time was precious.

'Cormac wants me back.' Yolande played her master card with a flourish. 'We got together again at the conference. It was a wonderful experience, making my affairs with all the other men I've known seem like kiss-and-hold hands. I've broken with the man I've been living with, and I'm doing as Cormac wants—I'm going back to him.'

Lynda moistened her lips. 'But he's still at the conference. There was an important meeting, he said.' It was all she could think of to say while her mind tried vainly to grapple with the devastating news which this ex-fiancée of Cormac's had fed into it.

'Which reminds me.' Yolande adjusted the drape of her skirt. 'He told me to tell you he won't be going back to Whitegates. He'll be taking up residence for a while at his London apartment.' She inspected her scarlet nails as if testing them for depth of colour. 'He's asked me to live with him, and I'm going to. As from tonight.' It was in the nature of a final shoot-to-kill.

Yolande rose to her feet and floated across to the door. Lynda could think of nothing to say. Hadn't Betty Peters tried to warn her? And hadn't she thought—with such foolishly false confidence, it seemed—that she could deal with a dozen women like this one?

Betty hurried in when Yolande had gone. 'I wanted to warn you, Mrs Daly, but she didn't give me a chance.' She was concerned at Lynda's pale face and stunned expression. 'What's she been saying to you, that—that venomous woman? Brandy, Mrs Daly? No? Take no notice of her——'

'Does Mr Daly own a London apartment, Betty?'

The secretary nodded, giving the answer Lynda had dreaded. Why hadn't he told her of its existence? And had her quarrel with him the other evening on the telephone been the turning-point, causing him to decide to take his ex-fiancée back, shedding the wife he had taken on simply to revenge himself against the woman who had let him down so cruelly?

'It's near Regent's Park, Mrs Daly. A beautiful place. I went there once.'

'Thanks, Betty.' The secretary withdrew. Lynda held her head—a thousand hammers were turning her inner world into a living hell. So what now? A period of time, divorce proceedings, then a lifetime's un-happiness stretching in front of her. Worst of all, her mind cried out, why didn't he tell me himself? Why did he have to humiliate me by getting his woman to carry the message, one which was passed on so casually?

Lynda did not go to her mother's that evening. It would have been impossible not to pour out her heart, and she did not want to burden her mother with her own troubles. She would have to be told, but not yet, not until she had thought out her own—and, she realised with a shock, her mother's—future.

When the phone rang, her feet could not take her to answer it fast enough. It just had to be Cormac, putting an end to this nightmare of uncertainty and doubt. It was Larry Chapman.

'Lynda. I want to do a deal with you.' He spoke with a curious authority and it worried her. 'Something I want to talk over. Come out with me, just a drink and a chat.'

She found herself agreeing before she had had time to consider the implications of his words. He would call for her, he said, in half an hour. He lived in her direction, he told her.

Watching his car approach along the drive, she felt only half aware of what she was intending to do. At the invitation of the man who had harmed the careers of at least two women—herself and a girl called Amy—she was going out with him to talk over some unspecified deal. When she had last spoken to him on the telephone, he had done his best to insult her, so why had she accepted his invitation now?

He was politeness itself, showing her into his car as though it were a Rolls-Royce.

As they drove, she named one or two country inns in the vicinity. He nodded, but drove on, talking generalities. When they reached the outskirts of suburbia, Lynda voiced her fears.

'Just a drink, you said, Larry.'

'At my place, did I forget to mention? You don't mind, Lynda, do you?' He smiled, but Lynda did not like the look his eyes held. It was a situation she now had no choice but to accept, and he knew it. He turned into a side street and she realised they were almost there.

The block of flats was reasonably modern, and his apartment was as modest as his car. He apologised for the lack of room. 'It's the best I can afford. I put all the spare cash I've got into my business.'

Lynda nodded her understanding, wishing at the same time that she could understand why he was so anxious to talk to her. He put a drink into her hand, guided her to a chair and took a seat himself, sitting forward.

'A key word—Kitchenware.' He held up his hand, stopping her protest before it began. 'Okay, so I remember the last time I mentioned it, you refused. No deal.'

'So why bring me all this way to talk about it again?'

He waved his arm airily. 'Rumours I've heard.'

Lynda paled. 'What rumours?'

'Your husband's left you, hasn't he?' The words, spoken so bluntly, were like a bucket of ice water thrown over her to sober her up. Mentally, she reeled. The haze cleared, the truth, sharply outlined, stared right back at her. Cormac had left her. Their marriage was over.

'Who told you?' She had meant to say it defiantly, but it came out as a whisper.

'Yolande. I called her this morning at the conference she was attending. I wanted to ask her if she was willing to do this modelling job you wouldn't do. She told me no, because she'd gone back to Cormac. Which could only mean one thing—he'd left you. So you'd need the money, I calculated.'

'You calculated wrong, Larry. I don't need that kind of money.'

'Why, has Daly paid you off already? Big settlement, provided you with a penthouse suite, bought your silence?'

Lynda snapped her teeth together. 'Do you always get what you want by insulting the people you're trying to do a deal with?'

'Point taken,' was Larry's unabashed answer. 'So you're ready for that deal?'

'No again.'

'Look, Lynda,' his manner had quietened, 'all I want is to take some shots of you, nice background, pretty pictures. Barbecue by the pool.'

'Housewife at leisure? I've heard that before, from Rodge, except that he didn't know—still doesn't—that I was the female in the Kitchenware ad. By the pool?'

she queried. 'Don't tell me you want that "leisurely housewife" in a two-piece swimsuit?' He nodded and she sighed. 'Again, we've been here before, Larry.'

He shook his head slowly. 'If you say so.' A thought hit him. 'There's a way round it. If I took those shots of you, then superimposed another model's head and features over yours, no one would know it was you.'

'Photographic trickery? Like you promised with that girl called Amy? Sorry, Larry. You let her down, and you could let me down in the same way. Will you please take "no"? I mean it.'

The phone rang and Larry answered it. 'Oh, hi, Yolande. About that modelling? No, no luck. Yes, Lynda's here. Or should I say Mrs Daly?' He gave Lynda a sly glance. 'Why's she here? For a drink, a chat, and—well, use your imagination.'

Lynda sprang at the phone, trying to wrestle the receiver from Larry's hand. 'Cormac's there, at his London apartment. He must be back from the conference by now. I want to speak to him, do you hear?'

He held her off by grasping her shoulder with more strength than Lynda imagined he possessed. 'Sorry, Yolande. That was Lynda getting jealous because I'm talking to you. She wants me all to herself. 'Bye now.'

'You miserable——'

He put a finger to her lips, but she seized his hand, twisting it until he swore. Then she picked up her bag and left his apartment, taking a taxi all the way home.

CHAPTER TEN

It took all of Lynda's courage to go into work the next day. It was inevitable that she and Cormac would meet, since her office was next to his.

Before venturing into her own room, she called on Betty. 'Is my husband here yet?' she asked, then realised how strange the question might sound from a wife whose husband had been due back the night before.

Betty shook her head, unsurprised. 'The message I got was that he'd been delayed in Manchester. A business matter—new client, probably.'

Lynda sighed, relief mingling with disappointment. If they had met, she would have been able to explain . . . And, she thought with a leap of her heart, he would deny everything Yolande had said about going back to live with him.

He did not appear the following day, either, but there was a letter waiting, unopened, marked 'strictly personal' on Lynda's desk. There was no address, just her name, Mrs Lynda Daly. It was handwritten, and Lynda recognised Cormac's writing instantly.

'Lynda,' the letter ran, 'Consider our marriage at an end. I do not want to see you again. Consider your employment with the company terminated as from this morning. Your mother can remain in the cottage. Whether or not you decide to share it with her is your decision. From all I have heard about your extra-marital activities, you will probably not. My decision is that you leave my house at once. My allowance to you will continue until after the divorce, when maintenance will no doubt be decided by the court. Cormac.'

Lynda's hand started shaking as it held the curt communication. 'Dismissal notice,' she thought bitterly, from her husband's life. Consider their marriage had ended—just like that, without giving her a single chance to speak in her own defence? Extra-marital activities? He couldn't mean she was having an affair with Larry Chapman?

Who else? she thought. And who else had told him but Yolande Wilson, his ex-fiancée, *his present lover*? She would not allow him to be so self-righteous, she would not be dismissed from his life without even a trial!

Picking up her phone, hand still trembling, she asked Betty Peters if she would telephone the hotel at which her husband was staying in Manchester. A few minutes later Betty answered her query.

'Mr Daly isn't there, Mrs Daly. He checked out lunchtime on Monday.'

'Two days ago? But I thought you told me——'

'He was delayed there. I don't understand it any more than you do.'

Bewildered, they stared at each other. There was one person she could ask. She would ring him now. 'I'll see what I can find out, Betty, then let you know.' Still frowning, the secretary returned to her room.

Lynda dialled and waited. 'Rodge——' She had to take a breath. Her mind was parrying the blows being aimed at it one by one like a tennis player desperately returning well-aimed balls across the net. Not one of them must hit her, the impact would be too disastrous. Later, she thought, later I'll let them hit their target.

'Hi, Lynda,' he said, and waited patiently.

'Tell me something, Rodge. You must tell me!' She was near to hysteria now and Rodge must have heard it.

'Calm down. I'll help if I can.'

'Just tell me where Cormac is, Rodge. *Please. . . !*' Her voice almost broke.

'Take it easy there! Lynda, I don't know. At a conference, I was told. Didn't he come back last night?'

'I've got a letter from him, Rodge—a terrible letter.'

She was forced to stop by the threatening tears. 'He's going to divorce me.'

'But it was on the cards, sweetheart,' he said in a kindly way. 'You as good as told me the other night.' It was no use, she couldn't answer. 'I'll do some investigating, then come back to you. Okay?'

She mumbled her thanks, put down the phone and waited, staring at the moist drops as they hit the page of the letter open in front of her.

When the phone rang again, she reached out. 'Rodge?'

'I've discovered his whereabouts. He's in hospital in London.' He gave its name.

'Oh God, no! He's been injured? He's had a fall and his leg——'

'Is being operated on to remove the bits and pieces.'

That operation for which he had been waiting, the one that would bring with it the beginning of the end of their marriage. What an irony, she thought, that the ending of their marriage should come first.

The silence was so long, Rodge asked, 'Like me to come up to your office and have a talk?'

'Thanks, but it wouldn't do any good. It's all too involved to explain, but the fact remains that he doesn't want me any more, anyway.' She was doing her best to sound resigned, but it was an unconvincing effort.

Four weeks passed, four of the hardest weeks of Lynda's life. When she had told her mother about the ending of her marriage, Rose had not believed it.

'It's not possible, Lynda. He's such a kind man. He's been good to me, wonderful to you. There's been a misunderstanding,' she had ended confidently. 'When he comes back from hospital, it will all be explained, you'll see.'

Cormac had not come home from hospital. He must long ago have left there, Lynda estimated. He had instead gone to live with his girl-friend, not his wife. And she did not even know the address of his London apartment!

Mrs Wendon had been dismayed to hear of the break-up, refusing almost to believe it. 'Mr Daly just isn't like that,' she had protested. 'I've known him for years, dear. He wouldn't do something so terrible to a lady like you. And someone he loves so much!'

Lynda had smiled tiredly, shaking her head. Cormac must indeed have loved her a lot, to desert her the moment his ex-fiancée beckoned. The housekeeper had continued to look after the house, even though Lynda no longer lived there.

Every day, Mrs Wendon went across to help Rose, often making a meal for her, to save her 'poor old hands,' as she put it.

Lynda was lost without a job to go to. It was not so long ago, she remembered, that she had found herself in just that same situation, brought about by that same man. But then, she had had that address, the address which had held such promise.

Late one evening, she wandered back to the house. In every room, she summoned up a vision of Cormac, working or relaxing or listening to music, the music they had shared that final evening when they had made such passionate love.

It hurt her most of all to look around the bedroom. There, she did not need to use her imagination—he was everywhere. She felt him, strong and virile, his arms opened wide to receive her. Reality hit her, its sting bringing tears. She went blindly to the window, staring out at the darkening landscape.

A movement behind her brought her pivoting round. A man stood in the doorway. He was tall and lean and tanned, and he was standing squarely on his two feet. Nothing supported him except his legs, straight and strong.

'Cormac! You're fit and well!' The words burst from her. 'You can walk alone again!' Her arms strained towards him as if puppet strings were tugging her across to him. He ignored her spontaneous gesture and her arms fell to her sides.

His navy shirt was short-sleeved and partly unbuttoned. His jeans close-fitting and belted. His sun-browned arms were tough with dark hair and muscle. Yes, he could walk alone, this man with eyes of steel. There was nothing about him now that needed her help. He was independent in both body and mind, strong in resolve and a determination to follow that resoluteness through, even to the end, no matter how bitter it might be.

He walked a pace or two towards her. 'Why are you here?' he snarled. 'I thought I made it plain that all our ties were severed. Weren't my words specific enough—that I wanted you out of my house and out of my life?'

He was treading her happiness underfoot. She looked at him, aghast once more at his intractability. 'Cormac,' she whispered, pale-faced, 'why did you send me that terrible letter? What have I done to make you turn on me like that?'

'You ask me what you've done when it came to my knowledge that the "secret lover" you joked about existed in reality?'

'Tell me, Cormac, tell me who that so-called lover of mine is?'

He advanced towards her, hands pushed into his jeans pockets. His eyes burned through her, searing her heart. 'His name?' he rasped. 'Chapman, the man I fired because he took shots of you against my orders. And why did I write that letter? Because one of the evenings you were at his place, he told the caller you were with him and you were jealous because he was talking to her and you wanted him to yourself.'

'But that caller was Yolande. Cormac, how could you take the word of those two people? A man who uses others, at no matter what cost to them; and a woman who two-timed you, as you called it, by having a lover even while she was engaged to you.'

'You've proved you're two-faced, too. You're no better than they are.'

'By having a lover while being your wife? It's not

true, Cormac,' she caught at his shirt, 'it just isn't
true!' Her voice rose in her desperation to clear
herself.

He wrenched himself free of her clutching hold. 'It's
not true? So explain this.' He pulled a half-rolled
booklet from his back pocket. 'Tell me now you're not
two-faced!'

He tossed the booklet to her. It came open at
the centre spread. 'Kitchenware does it again' the
words proclaimed. 'Housewife at Leisure. Barbecue
by the pool.' Illustrating the new products were
photographs of herself in a two-piece swimsuit
reclining by a poolside wall, half-lying on an
inflatable bed, seated at a garden table beneath a
large, striped umbrella.

They were the shots Larry Chapman had taken of
her the day Cormac had appeared at the studio door
and instructed Larry to destroy the film. It was plain
that it was an instruction he had blatantly disobeyed.

'He kept the film,' she said, her voice thin. 'I had no
control over that, did I?'

His mouth twisted. 'Did you not?'

'What are you implying I've done? At least let me
know the crime I'm supposed to have committed.'

'I'm suggesting that, besides taking him as your
lover, you connived with him to supply Kitchenware
with the pictures of you they were searching for so
eagerly. I'm suggesting you knew he hadn't destroyed
that film.'

He went up to her and took her by the shoulders,
dragging her against him, forcing her to feel the angles
and unyielding hardness of his body.

'Was the allowance I made you not enough? Did you
have to supplement it by accepting the fat fee he gave
you from the large sum of money he no doubt exacted
from Kitchenware for the privilege of having the face
and body of the wife of the head of Daly Enterprises as
part of the promotion of their products?'

Letting the booklet fall to the floor, Lynda dropped
on to the bed, holding her head. She felt as if she had

been hit in the stomach by a professional boxer. Her throat was stiff, preventing her from speaking; her eyes were dry, so no tears came.

Her hands were dragged apart. 'Lift up your head. Look at me.' She raised her head, but her eyes stayed closed. Her cheeks felt cold, her body burning.

'Have I shattered your world,' his question came cruelly, 'by revealing all your devious little secrets?'

Her eyes came open, holding his hard stare. 'You have a secret. You've got a lover. You've taken Yolande Wilson back—which is why you wanted to get rid of me as your wife!' Her hands were freed although they still ached from his hold.

'Don't think,' he bit out, 'that by making fanciful accusations back at me that you can justify your own contemptible actions.'

'How can they be fanciful, when I heard them from Yolande herself? She came to the office. Ask Betty Peters.' Her head lifted proudly. 'Has your ex-fiancée been reinstated now?'

'There's been no reinstatement,' Cormac answered curtly.

'Which means you're content to go on living with her until you're legally free of me.'

'Who said I'm living with her?'

'Yolande Wilson herself told me. She said she "got together" with you at the conference. That can mean only one thing where she's concerned. She said you wanted her back and that she was going, as from that night—the last night of the conference when you were due to come home.'

'That night, I went into hospital.' He half-sat on the dressing-table. 'My leg had been giving me hell. I rang my doctor and told him I couldn't stand it any longer. He could see no reason for delaying the operation, since the repair of the injury was going so well.'

'So she was lying?' He nodded briefly. 'But when you came out of hospital, you probably went back to your London apartment?' He did not respond. 'That was where she told me she would be living.'

He continued to watch her. The fact that he had not denied this last accusation forced her to face reality yet again. She wasn't wanted in his life, so what was she doing there?

Pushing trembling fingers through her hair, she went to the door. 'Where are you going?' he asked.

'Out of your house and out of your life. That's what you said, wasn't it?'

'Come here, Lynda.'

She shook her head, but made one last effort to clear herself. 'Cormac, you must believe me—I never wanted money for its own sake. All I ever wanted, right from the start, was help for my mother. Go and see her now, as she really is. The break-up of our marriage has upset her so much she's let herself go. She looks ill, Cormac, which is how I saw her that day I decided to come to the address you'd given me—this house—as a last hope of finding employment.'

'Come here, I said.' His eyes held a glint, and his voice compelled her to obey.

She stood in front of him. 'I'll get out of your life. You can keep your money. All I want is for my mother to keep her cottage. In return, at least be honest with me and admit that you and Yolande have come together again.'

While she had been speaking, his manner had undergone a subtle change. 'It's untrue, Lynda, every single word of it.'

In spite of herself, her heart lifted. 'Why should I believe you, any more than you believe me?'

'There's a simple answer to that.' The glint in his eyes had turned into a gleam. His arms claimed her, wrapping round her and holding her to him. 'If our minds refuse to be at peace with each other, let our bodies try to bridge the chasm. I'm going to make love to you, Lynda.' His hand held her chin, and his mouth caught urgently at her closed lips. 'Let me kiss you, my love,' he urged huskily. 'I'm like a starving man, reaching out. Not for a crumb, or a scrap, but for the whole of you. You don't know what you did to me that first time I saw you. From that moment, I was determined to have you.'

'Wanted,' she thought, 'determined to have me' ... Not a word of love to sweeten the hardness of his desire, but when his mouth moved on hers again, she parted her lips to his forceful exploration. His hands moved over her as though he was learning the feel of her all over again. Impatient with the barriers formed by her clothes, he tore at buttons, tugged at zips, peeled away layers, then she stood naked against him.

He held her away and looked at her breasts which had filled and blossomed to hardness under his touch. His palm ran the length of her and she shivered with desire for their mutual fulfilment.

'Lynda, my love, stay as honest as you are, never let me down.' His kisses warmed her throat, her body, the heart beneath her ribs.

He had called her honest! 'I promise, oh, darling, I promise I'll never leave you or let you down. I love you too much ...'

'Remove my shirt,' he commanded, and she pushed it from his shoulders. His belt buckle opened under her moist fingers. As she progressed, she looked up at him shyly, crouching low to finish the undressing, kissing the scars on his leg.

Cormac bent down and lifted her, swinging her into his arms and holding her high. He stood firm and steady on his two legs, using the strength he had been forced for so long to keep in check.

On the bed, he put her beneath him, finding her inner thighs with his hand and coaxing them to a throbbing life. She ached with the need for him and when he came into her, moving thrustingly to bring her body to a joyous awareness, she lost all sense of time and place and was conscious only of her unbounded love for the man who was bringing her to the pinnacle of happiness.

Satiated—for the moment, Cormac had murmured—they lay in each others' arms. Their limbs were entangled and Lynda had the strangest feeling that they were really one, merged into a single entity.

'Cormac?' Her finger traced the line of his mouth, then she put a kiss where her finger had been. The lips formed into the faintest of smiles.

'Mm?' he asked in a lazy voice.

'Why did you send me that letter? I asked you before, but you didn't answer.'

He pulled her on to him. 'Must you talk? I'd rather do this,' his hand ran over her back, coming to rest on the soft mound of her rear, 'and this,' his hands moved upwards to massage her breasts which pressed against his chest.

'I must talk, Cormac,' she answered breathlessly, feeling an ache begin low down. 'Please tell me.'

He rolled her beside him. 'Point one, I did not "get together" with Yolande at that conference. She did her very best in that respect, but I told her to get lost and that I loved the woman I'd married.'

'Cormac, you love me?'

He gazed at her in astonishment. 'What do you think all this——' he indicated the rumpled bed '—is all about, if it wasn't done with love? And why did I give you this,' he held the gold band on her wedding finger, 'if not because I loved you enough to marry you?'

'So why did you keep Yolande's photograph?'

'To remind me of the treachery of women,' he answered, his voice hard.

'When I objected to it, you didn't throw it out, did you? I found it in your drawer.'

'If you'd looked farther down that drawer, you would have found your own.'

'That one of me in the Kitchenware brochure?'

'That one exactly. The picture of the girl I looked at that first day caught my fancy so hard I shouted— with anger, please note,' his hand fitted round her throat, lifting her mouth for his kiss, 'because I'd vowed that no woman would get through my guard ever again.'

'And I did?' His answer was in his eyes. 'Now I know you love me.' She settled more comfortably into his arms. After a while, she remarked, 'Yolande told me she still had power over your reflexes.'

'Oh, did she? Well, she did—over my aggressive ones, my anger. She insisted on seeing me that Monday I went into hospital. She told me about her conversation on the phone with Chapman. She added, like throwing a knife and hitting dead on target, that you were with him. She recounted what he told her about the two of you. You know the rest.'

Lynda nodded. 'When you came out of hospital, did you go to your London apartment?'

'No, I went to the south of France for a week or so to get over the operation. Part of my recovery programme was to exercise and walk.'

'Which is why you're so tanned.'

'And fit enough to satisfy my wife,' he held her the length of him, 'many times over.' Tightening his hold, he added, 'I thought about our relationship. Frankly, I didn't know how I was going to live without you.'

Lynda just held on to him, her fingertips making dents in his flesh. 'When did you first know you loved me?'

'I fell in love with the girl whose shape was spread so impudently across the two pages of the promotion blurb. I had to see her. Which is why I went to the office you were in. I wanted to see you exactly as you were, before you'd had a chance to do anything special to yourself.'

'Like putting on make-up, and a special outfit?'

'Exactly. But when you came to see me, my eyes were so prejudiced against the type of woman that photograph represented, I couldn't see you as you really were. Yolande had succeeded in warping my judgment of women out of all proportion.'

'I did tell you it wasn't really me, darling.'

'Do you think my mind where women were concerned was balanced enough to accept your statement?'

'Which is why you sacked me?'

'There were other reasons. I gave you that address,

this address. Remember? It was my subconscious mind setting a trap I knew you'd fall into sooner or later. And you did, thank God.' His hold tightened still more.

'Why did you change your mind so drastically just now? While we were talking, I mean.'

'You said Yolande had told you she had gone back to me. I reasoned that if she could lie to you about that, she could have lied to me about other things.'

'Such as that non-existent affair with Larry?' He nodded. 'Why did you ever let yourself listen to her, then write that letter to me?'

'Imagine my situation. I was in hospital, about to undergo an operation. Also you and I had quarrelled a few days earlier on the phone. You'd mentioned a "secret lover" in anger. In the frame of mind I was in, I imagined that anything could be true. Hence the letter. Do you understand now?'

Lynda nodded, and he caught her face with his hand, parting her lips with his thumb and placing his own on top of them. After a while, she said, nestling into him,

'Rodge was a great help, darling. Do you know that he and my friend Mandy have got together?'

'Did I remember to tell you,' Cormac interrupted, 'that they're going to get married?'

'I'm delighted,' Lynda answered happily. 'It didn't take long for Rodge to get the dust of one woman off his hands before taking on another, did it?'

'If that's a dig at me, lady, it's hardly a fair comparison!'

Lynda laughed, then asked, 'May I have my job back?'

'You want a career before you have our kids? You shall have it.'

'Thanks, darling,' she whispered, then looked up at him impishly. 'Now I can carry on my—er——' she held his hands so that he couldn't touch her '—liaison with Mr Colling of Home-aid Planners.'

He easily freed his hands and took her body in a

punishing hold. 'You know what you're asking for, don't you?'

Eyes shining, she nodded. 'And I want it. I want you, Cormac.'

'You shall have me, my love. For ever.'

Take your holiday romance with you.

ROMANCE

Next month's romances from Mills & Boon

Each month, you can choose from a world of variety in romance with Mills & Boon. These are the new titles to look out for next month.

DON'T CALL IT LOVE Lindsay Armstrong
DARK AWAKENING Sally Wentworth
TWO DOZEN RED ROSES Rosemary Hammond
THE ODDS AGAINST Margaret Pargeter
SCANDALOUS Charlotte Lamb
ONCE FOR ALL TIME Betty Neels
DAWN OF A NEW DAY Claudia Jameson
DESPERATE DESIRE Flora Kidd
DOUBLE DOUBTING Jeneth Murrey
A PLACE CALLED RAMBULARA Margaret Way
THE DARLING JADE Peggy Nicholson
AND BLOW YOUR HOUSE DOWN Emma Goldrick

Buy them from your usual paperback stockist, or write to: Mills & Boon Reader Service, P.O. Box 236, Thornton Rd, Croydon, Surrey CR9 3RU, England. Readers in South Africa write to: Mills & Boon Reader Service of Southern Africa, Private Bag X3010, Randburg, 2125.

Mills & Boon
the rose of romance

Take 4 Exciting Books Absolutely FREE

Love, romance, intrigue... all are captured for you by Mills & Boon's top-selling authors. By becoming a regular reader of Mills & Boon's Romances you can enjoy 6 superb new titles every month plus a whole range of special benefits: your very own personal membership card, a free monthly newsletter packed with recipes, competitions, exclusive book offers and a monthly guide to the stars, plus extra bargain offers and big cash savings.

AND an Introductory FREE GIFT for YOU.
Turn over the page for details.

As a special introduction we will send you four exciting Mills & Boon Romances Free and without obligation when you complete and return this coupon.

At the same time we will reserve a subscription to Mills & Boon Reader Service for you. Every month, you will receive 6 of the very latest novels by leading Romantic Fiction authors, delivered direct to your door. You don't pay extra for delivery — postage and packing is always completely Free. There is no obligation or commitment — you can cancel your subscription at any time.

You have nothing to lose and a whole world of romance to gain.

Just fill in and post the coupon today to **MILLS & BOON READER SERVICE, FREEPOST, P.O. BOX 236, CROYDON, SURREY CR9 9EL.**

Please Note:- **READERS IN SOUTH AFRICA write to Mills & Boon, Postbag X3010, Randburg 2125, S. Africa.**

FREE BOOKS CERTIFICATE

To: **Mills & Boon Reader Service, FREEPOST, P.O. Box 236, Croydon, Surrey CR9 9EL.**

Please send me, free and without obligation, four Mills & Boon Romances, and reserve a Reader Service Subscription for me. If I decide to subscribe I shall, from the beginning of the month following my free parcel of books, receive six new books each month for £6.60, post and packing free. If I decide not to subscribe, I shall write to you within 10 days. The free books are mine to keep in any case. I understand that I may cancel my subscription at any time simply by writing to you. I am over 18 years of age.

Please write in BLOCK CAPITALS.

Signature _____

Name _____

Address _____

_____ Post code _____

SEND NO MONEY — TAKE NO RISKS.

Please don't forget to include your Postcode.

Remember, postcodes speed delivery. Offer applies in UK only and is not valid to present subscribers. Mills & Boon reserve the right to exercise discretion in granting membership. If price changes are necessary you will be notified.

6R   *Offer expires July 31st 1984.*

EP86